The
Lonesome Whistle's
Call

The Lonesome Whistle's Call

Forced to leave home, a teenager rides the rails
during depression years

Stella E. Burns

Kingston Press

P. O. Box 86, West Kingston, RI 02892-0086

Illustrations by Evelyn Kenyon, Wakefield, RI

ISBN 0-9660247-0-2
Library of Congress Catalog Card Number: 97-092572

Dedicated
to my husband
Scottie Burns
who rode the rails when a teenager.
His stories have inspired this book
and he has stood on the sidelines
cheering me on to
its completion.

I wish to acknowledge
the illustrations by Evelyn Kenyon
and thank her for her patience;
I thank my grandson Alex Burns
who drew the silhouette of a hobo
shown in the book;
and
Jack Whitford for his editing
and helpful suggestions.

TABLE OF CONTENTS

PART I
FROM CHILDHOOD TO TEENAGER

PART II
RIDING THE RAILS

LIST OF ILLUSTRATIONS
AND PHOTOS

Travel

The railroad track is miles away,
    and the day is loud with voices speaking,
Yet there isn't a train goes by all day
    But I hear its whistle shrieking.

All night there isn't a train goes by,
    Though the night is still for sleep and dreaming,
But I see its cinders red on the sky,
    and hear its engine steaming.

My heart is warm with the friends I make,
    And better friends I'll not be knowing,
Yet there isn't a train I wouldn't take,
    No matter where it's going.

-- Edna St. Vincent Millay

FOREWORD

In *"The Lonesome Whistle's Call"* Stella Burns has given us a compelling picture of Depression era America through the travels and exploits of her husband Scottie. The vivid and heartbreaking description of the dirt poor family in its struggles to survive is reminiscent of the Joad family in John Steinbeck's *The Grapes of Wrath* and the flight from the tyrannical father onto a journey of self-discovery summons comparisons with Mark Twain's national epic *The Adventures of Huckleberry Finn.* Like Huck's odyssey into manhood which begins with a feigned drowning, young Edward Burns' transformation also begins with a sort of baptism in which the "old self" is forsaken and the new identity of "Scottie" is born. Other literary parallels to Twain's young hero are also evident, but rather than dissect the story for its "deeper meanings," I would invite the reader to come aboard and share with Scottie his exciting adventures as he rides the rails of freedom and meets up with as colorful a band of ragtag humanity as one is likely to find anywhere. For those old enough to remember, *The Lonesome Whistle's Call* is a ticket to ride back into bittersweet memory; for those too young, it is an adventure into a shared reality now retreating into the past. For everyone, however, it is a fascinating and enjoyable experience.

Jack Whitford, teacher of English and Creative Writing

PART I
FROM CHILDHOOD TO TEENAGER

The Long Ride South

Jane held a cool damp cloth to her forehead as she wearily plunked into the rocking chair next to the baby. The temperature had reached a humid 90º on this August day in East Greenwich, Rhode Island. Listlessly she watched her two young sons at play. Five year old Edward lay on his stomach on the floor, slowly pushing a crude wooden train 'round and 'round the small oval braided rug. He quickly abandoned the toy when a loud shrill whistle signaled and the house convulsed uncontrollably. Cups and plates clinked together on the sideboard.

"The train!" he whooped scrambling to his feet and running to the low window to peer through its small, jaundiced, time-worn panes. Above a thick green screen of trees and brush, clouds of black smoke and cinders bunched up, filling the sky with darkness. Within minutes, the clouds dispersed, leaving gray wisps like giant brush strokes across an azure blue canvas. With one last shuddering groan, the house settled back onto its foundation.

"I couldn't see the train!" the disappointed boy whined, stamping his foot on the rough wooden floor. "I wanted to see train!"

"Well, it's gone!" Jane snapped as she scooped up baby Laura. "Go play with your brother." Edward gyrated and squealed when he turned and saw three year old Parnell holding his train.

"Put it down! It's mine!" he yelled. Suddenly the toy train became the object of a tug-of-war, stretching between the boys like a fat clothesline. "Mom!" they screamed in unison. Laura, who had been nursing at Jane's breast looked up with wide startled eyes.

"Now you've frightened your sister," Jane sighed. "Let Parnell play with the train for a while." Holding the end of the train above his head, Edward let go of the caboose.

1

"Ow!" Parnell shrieked as the train slammed into his leg. Edward's only concern was that one of its wheels broke off and rolled out of sight under the couch.

"You broke my train!" Edward bawled. Grabbing Parnell's metal truck, he angrily thrust it against his brother's leg. Parnell lunged at his older brother with clenched fists. Tumbling around the floor, they pulled and tugged at each other like puppies at play.

"The train broke when you hit Parnell with it!" Jane's voice rose to a high frustrated pitch. "Now stop fighting or you'll both go to bed!" Edward plunked onto the floor and scrutinized his brother with squinted eyes and tight lips.

To these boys this house and the make-believe world of riding trains and driving trucks was their life. They were oblivious to the abject poverty blanketing America in 1927. They did not know, nor did they care, that it was a daily struggle to keep the family together. Even before the Stock Market crash and the official Depression of 1929, jobs were scarce in New England. Edward's father "Coop" (short for Cooper), along with hundreds of others, shifted occupations and took lesser pay or arrived hours before opening time at the factory gates to stand in line hoping to get a job. Then they returned to their homes no better off than they had been the day before and the week before that.

"Car come!" Parnell called as a Model T noisily wound its way up the bumpy driveway. Father was home. Edward dashed upstairs like a frightened rabbit. Lying on the hallway floor, he pressed his face against the metal heating grate and observed the kitchen below. Although he didn't want to be in the room with his father, he still was curious as to what was going on downstairs.

Jane put Laura down, glanced in the small cracked mirror on the wall, smoothed her hair and went to greet Coop at the door. Edward's heart beat rapidly as his father roughly shoved his mother aside and marched in. Glad to be upstairs away from this man who struck him many times for reasons he did not understand, Edward grimaced as his father slipped on Parnell's metal truck and awkwardly grabbed the counter to balance himself.

"Damn kids! Never take care of their toys!" Coop yelled. "I could 'ave been kilt." Angrily snatching up Edward's train he threw it into the fire of the wood burning cook stove.

"That was my toy," Edward murmured. Sitting with his back

against the wall, he hugged his body tightly. Even though it was Parnell's truck that had tripped his Pa, his wooden train had been unfairly thrown away. Briskly grinding both fists into his eye sockets stopped the hot tears from streaming down his cheeks, for he believed his Pa would give him a lickin' if he heard him cry. "That was my toy," he whispered over and over while rocking his body back and forth.

It suddenly dawned on Edward that the house was filled with an uncanny silence, a silence that could be felt. It was so intense that it frightened him. Quietly crawling back to the grate, he stared down at his father, mother and Parnell. They were standing within arm's reach of each other, but no one was touching. No one was moving. No one was talking. It's like they're dead or made of stone he thought.

"You didn't find anything at all?" Jane's voice shattered the deep stillness as she gently reached out and placed her hand on Coop's arm. He shook it off as though it were a poison spider.

"Yeah, sure, I found somethin'. Found out they ain't hirin'! I'm damn sick of having' doors slammed in my face. What in hell's a man to do?" Forcefully shoving his wife away from him, he continued, "I just got myself into a mess marryin' you. Musta been out of my mind." Edward's heart raced with panic and uncertainty as Jane turned toward the window and starting sobbing.

"Please God, don't let my Pa hurt Mama," he prayed. Although he wasn't sure if there was a God who heard him or not, praying and wishing was all he could do.

Weakly, Coop plunked into a kitchen chair. His hands trembled as he supported his bowed head. Several minutes later, he unexpectedly threw his arms into the air. "They'll call me if'n somethin' comes up!" Coop's words boomed through the house. Edward cringed back against the wall while his father continued to rage. "We ain't got no telephone and they give a stupid answer like that. Just a bunch of smart asses, jerkin' me 'round!"

"Maybe tomorrow will be better," Jane's voice trembled as she looked at her husband through tear-filled eyes.

"Yeah, sure. Are yah stupid? There are *no* jobs. Can't yah get that through your head? I've got to go where there's work."

"Where's that?! Where can we go?!"

Edward shivered at the panic in his mother's voice.

"Rumor has it they're hirin' in Florida. Houses goin' up all over the place. I'm going' there and hire on as a carpenter."

3

"But," Jane hesitated, "... suppose you don't get hired?"

"Bettah than stayin' here and dyin'!" His Pa had raised his voice again. "Pound nails. That's all yah hafta do!"

Without warning his whole demeanor changed again. Grinning and jumping to his feet he grabbed Jane by the waist and hugged her. Twirling around in an odd sort of dance, he shouted, "Florida, here we come!"

"Coop! Stop. Think," Jane gasped. "We can't go to Florida with three kids and no money!" Putting her hands on his chest she pushed him away. Coop let his arms hang limply to his sides and his features hardened into a frown as he plunked down again. Jane's face turned chalk white as she grasped the back of a chair. Edward was surprised his Pa didn't take a swing at his Ma for talking to him like that.

"We'll take the Model T. Go far's it takes us. No sense waitin'. We'll be out of this hell-hole tomorrow." He paused briefly and stared at Parnell and Laura. "Wish we didn't have these brats to drag along. Know anyone who'll take 'em?"

Jane shrieked like a woman gone mad. "I'll not give up the children. They stay with me!" She picked up Laura protectively while Parnell clutched her skirt.

"Can't you give it one more try?" Jane begged.

"NO!" he shouted, facing her with clenched fists. Jane dragged Parnell with her as she quickly retreated to the other side of the room. "Nothin' to be gained by stayin'," he continued. "You go or stay. Makes no nevah mind to me. I'm leavin' come daybreak." Edward knew his mother would go along with his father's plan, for she always ended up doing whatever he wanted. Everyone in the house was afraid of him and always obeyed when he spoke.

Cautiously Jane placed Laura back in the drawer used as a makeshift crib and sat Parnell in a chair before she ladled the contents of a small pot onto her husband's plate. He noisily slurped down the stewed venison and potatoes while Jane spread a thin layer of jelly on four slices of bread. Balancing the sandwiches in one hand she climbed the stairs with Parnell clinging tightly to her other hand.

"Edward! Get away from that grate! Eat your sandwich and hop into bed." Edward silently followed his mother into the room he shared with his brother and slowly ate his sandwich while he watched Jane throw clothes into an old black beat-up suitcase. The boys weren't tired

4

and it wasn't even dark when they climbed into bed fully clothed. Although the room was steaming hot, Edward pulled his blanket tightly around him like a cocoon and waited until he heard his mother going down the creaky stairs. Sneaking back to the grate, he watched his father drumming his fingertips on the table top while his mother gazed blankly at the clock ticking on the wall.

The minutes seemed like hours before Jane said softly, "I better pick the garden come daylight. Take vegetables with us."

"Nope! Can't do it!" Coop yelled as he smashed his fist onto the table. Laura screamed. Jane quickly picked her up and held her gently to her breast.

"Why not!" Jane talked unusually loud and fast. "They're ready to pick. We're not just leavin' ..." Their eyes locked like two bantam cocks ready to fly at each other. Coop spread his hands out on the table and pushed himself up from the chair.

"We're leavin' them. They're sold."

"You sold them? To who! We need that food!" Jane cried hysterically. "Me and the kids worked hard in that garden! You can't just up and sell it!"

"Well, damn you 'n the kids! I *can* sell it and I *did* sell it! We need gas for the Model T wors'n we need that garden."

Jane sobbed uncontrollably and it surprised Edward when Coop lowered his voice and spoke to her softly.

"You take a few veg'tables, but Fat Jim bought it 'as stands' for $20.00."

"Twenty dollars. The seed and plowin' alone are worth more'n that," Jane whimpered as she wiped her eyes with her apron. "That's all he'd give?"

"Yeah, that's all he'd give," he answered emphatically. "You think I'd take less if'n I could get more? You think I'm crazy?"

"No ... I didn't mean that, but ..."

"Jim'll be over early mornin'," Coop interrupted. "He'll notice if'n it's picked."

"What will *we* do for food?"

"We'll make out! Steal if we have to! Always askin' stupid questions."

Coop headed for the stairs without a backward glance at his wife. Scurrying to his bed, Edward listened to his mother's soft sobs. He

5

would've liked to have gone and hugged her, but instead he shut his eyelids tightly, covered his head with the blanket, and hugged his brother's sleeping body.

****

Activity downstairs woke Edward while the sky was still gray. It was time to start the day. While slowly descending the stairs he noticed his mother's red puffy eyes. "Today we're going to take a long ride, Edward," she said forcing a smile.

"Yes, M'am, I know." He was relieved that his father was nowhere in sight.

"Hurry and eat. I need your help in the garden," Jane said grabbing a towel that was draped over the back of a chair. Running outside, she left him to eat his cold oatmeal without milk or sugar.

Edward climbed down from the chair after the brown lump of cereal was all gone and his plate was scraped clean. The sun accentuated the gold highlights in his mother's hair as she knelt at the edge of the garden with the towel spread nearby. She showed him how to pick the green beans from under the leaves of the plants. Then she pulled some carrots and radishes while Edward carefully tamped down the earth. The little stash was wrapped in the towel before Jim drove up in his yellow Model A with a rumble seat. Jane held the bundle out to Edward.

"Put this on the floor in the back of our car," she whispered. He obediently strolled toward the Model T, keeping his eyes on the large man, hoping Jim wouldn't talk to him. There was no need to worry for the man was staring at Jane and didn't even glance at the boy.

"Mornin' Jim," Jane called to the man whose large belly appeared to have been forcefully jammed in between the steering wheel and the seat.

"Mornin'," he replied as he folded his "fat-man wheel" back so that he could heave himself out of the car. The metal frame of the Model A tilted and creaked under his weight as he stepped to the running board. Jane lowered her eyes and looked at the ground, conscious that Jim was studying her with his squinty eyes as he waddled across the yard. "Hope you know I'm doin' you a favor takin' this garden off your hands," the man bragged, piously looking at Coop who had just come from the outhouse.

"Ain't no favah to steal from a man!" Coop snapped back. Jim

6

ignored the remark and bent over and studied the garden before slowly picking a $20.00 bill from his plump brown wallet. He handed it to Coop without a word while his glistening blue eyes stared at Jane from under his bushy eyebrows.

Edward noticed how uncomfortable and flushed his mother looked. As she lowered her head, her auburn hair fell across her face and she self-consciously folded her arms across her breasts. Coop, irritated by Fat Jim's observance of his wife, signaled Jane with a jerky motion of his head to get into the "T". She quickly went to the house and got the children. Jim just stood gawking at the family while they struggled to pack the automobile.

"See you're loaded and ready to go," Jim remarked when they had tied on the last article.

After climbing into the Model T, Coop called out to Jim, "Could yah give the crank a turn?" Smiling brazenly at Jane, the man gave the Model T a couple of hefty rotations while Coop worked the choke. The "T" coughed, sputtered, and then steadily purred. With Coop, Jane, three children, clothing, pots and pans inside; mattresses, blankets and boxes securely tied to the roof; and jugs of water and suitcases tied to the running boards, they clattered out onto the open road--headed south for Florida. Edward pressed his nose against the glass and watched the familiar surroundings grow smaller in the distance. His heart thumped and he sat back against the seat when his father spoke harshly.

"I saw the way that pig Jim looked at you!" Coop leaned over and screamed at his wife like he thought she was deaf. "Yah been givin' him cause to look at you?" Edward wondered why his father was so angry about Jim looking at his mother. It wasn't her fault what the man did.

"Of course not. Don't be silly. Why'd I want that fat man?"

"You're my woman. Yah know what I'd do if'n yah cheated on me?" He roughly grabbed her arm leaving red impressions from his finger tips on her flesh.

"Coop, you're hurtin' me. There's nothin' between Jim and me."

"Bettah not be," Coop retorted as he released his grip and struck her arm with the palm of his hand.

The noise from the engine and the clatter of pans were the only sounds for several miles as the Model T bounced over the rough road. Edward sat silently staring straight ahead lost in his own thoughts, hardly daring to move.

"I've got to go pee," Parnell whimpered.

"Mom, Parnell's got to pee," Edward whispered, tugging at his mother's shoulder.

"He'll just have to wait!" Coop barked. "We're not stoppin' 'til we need gas. Sit back and shut up!" Both boys obediently shrunk back against the scratchy horsehair seat.

~ ~ ~

A *Journal* Account

After traveling for many weary days, the family reached Pensacola, Florida. Edward was ecstatic at his first sight of the ocean. It seemed to go forever until it blended with the edge of the sky. Huge waves edged in white foam rolled in, lapping the beach like a giant dog's tongue. Then the waves flattened, ran over the sand and were drawn back into the ocean again. Edward felt sheer enjoyment as the cool wet sand squished between his toes. He stood amazed at how his footprints were gobbled up by the incoming waves. Further up the beach, he ran dry sand through his fingers and collected rocks and shells. The boy was happier than he had ever been in his life. He just wanted to run ... run ... run. Ignoring his family, Coop was entertaining a group of folk bragging about his penniless trip from Rhode Island to Florida.

"Hey, mister, get your car out of the water!" someone shouted.

Edward stopped his playing and watched the people running toward his mother and father. Amazingly the water was surging up over the running board. Men and women pushed and pulled the "tin lizzy" while Coop spun the wheels deeper into the sand. In the end, the tide and power of the ocean won. Edward's family watched with horror as the Model T with most of their belongings still tied to it turned over and disappeared into the immense ocean.

"Damn!" Coop screamed turning to Jane who stood like a lost child clutching Laura and a pillow case bulging with what clothing she had snatched from the "T".

"Why didn't yah let me know tide was comin' in? Ain't worth much are yah?"

Humiliated before these strangers, Jane wilted. She couldn't hold her tears back. They flowed uncontrollably from her tired eyes. "I didn't see, Coop. I couldn't help it," she sobbed.

"I'm sorry, Mama" Edward said as he ran to her side. She silently looked down at him with dull unseeing eyes.

"I'm headin' for town!" Coop's voice boomed out like a clap of thunder. He turned and angrily knocked the shells from Edward's hands. Grabbing the pillowcase from Jane, Coop shoved it toward Edward. "Carry this," he growled as he stalked away. Jane, her body still shaking from fatigue and stress, gathered her children together and started after Coop. Edward dragged his feet, sadly looking back at his collection of shells strewn on the sand.

In Pensacola the Salvation Army offered help. They housed and fed them until Coop landed a job. The following account appeared in the *Providence Journal,* November 16, 1930.*

"[His] dreams of wealth were not disappointed, for he [Coop] found work and plenty. Apartment houses were going up in the space around Pensacola, and he found plenty to do--at pay that was ample. When he wasn't working on some building project, he was helping on Government road work--hard surfacing roads that were stretching out there [for miles] ...

"Everything went well until the floods came. The papers were full of the disastrous tidings. River banks were overflowed and houses toppled over. Whole broadsides of pictures showed the wretched conditions along the rivers [in the South]. There was, fortunately, little loss of life.

"And one night [Coop] and his family found themselves in the attic of their little house, the flood surrounding them, and no way of escape. There was only one way out, and he found it--by chopping a hole in the roof. A day and a half or so they spent there, he says, the parents and children. Then boats came and took them off [the roof].

"How they got along for the next two weeks or months, he declares he can hardly tell. 'We went along with the rest of the mob,' he says, 'and got along somehow', and this precarious existence went on for months. There was no job and no money ... And one

---

* This account was written after the family returned to Rhode Island almost three years from the time of their departure for Florida.

*morning, without a leave or asking one--and without a nickel--
they simply went down to the station, found a freight bound
outward, and got in. There were a lot of other wayfarers doing
the same thing,' he says.*

*"And when the ride and the day were over and the railroad men
turned them out, they were ... [in Montgomery, Alabama] 96
miles [closer] toward their goal."*

****

Edward was boosted into the boxcar. With his head lowered, he
stood rooted to the spot, conscious of several men staring at him from
the far end of the car. When the train lurched forward, he was thrown
onto the wooden floor face first and the group of faceless men loudly
guffawed.

"Sit down, boy!" Coop commanded as he picked Edward up by the
back of his shirt and slammed him down next to his mother.

Coop, Jane, Edward, Parnell, Laura and Candice

11

The men huddled together inside the boxcar blended in with the siding ...

Edward soon forgot the rough treatment from his father for the train gave a jerk and started moving. The men huddled together inside the boxcar blended in with the siding and seemed far less threatening while he sat beside his mother and watched the scenery flash by. The whistles, the thundering power of the freight and fury of unleashed steam barking through the stacks won his heart. The continual clacking of the wheels was a happy rhythm to his ears. The world raced by at a speed that filled him with a sense of immense enjoyment. It was an excitement that the young boy would never forget.

When they reached Montgomery, the group of men in the car jumped to the gravel as the train slowed down. Edward watched wide-eyed when the railroad bulls swung their billy clubs and hit the men while chasing them into the brush surrounding the freight yard. He shrunk back away from the door, wondering if they were going to hit his family too. Fortunately, because of the children, the bulls pointed them to a Salvation Army that took them in.

Hard Times in Alabama

At the Salvation Army in Montgomery, Alabama, there were two rules that had to be observed: the family had to do odd jobs for their keep and they were required to attend the evening worship service before being given their supper. It was at one of these nightly meetings that a man sauntered in. Disrupting their hymn singing, he marched up to the front. The organist stopped playing and all eyes turned in his direction. He loudly proclaimed, "We're lookin' for workers to pick cotton. I'll be standin' outside to sign yah up if'n int'rested." After delivering his short message, he turned and left, rudely letting the door slam behind him.

Rev. Williamson, a tall gaunt elderly preacher, removed his black jacket and nervously shuffled papers as he prepared to preach. His ashen face and hands matched the color of the once white long-sleeved shirt he wore. Edward squirmed on the wooden bench, for the man's appearance and the hard seat both made him mighty uncomfortable.

"Hope he ain't too long winded," Coop said in a voice loud enough for all to hear. "Rather sleep in dirt than listen to his hogwash."

"Shhh!" Jane whispered. "It won't hurt you to listen to what the good Lord wants us to hear."

"Phmmpphh!" he snorted. "Wish he'd git on with it."

"He hears you, Coop," Jane whispered as her cheeks flushed with embarrassment. Coop looked up and his eyes defiantly locked with those of the preacher.

"Don't care," he replied, slumping down and letting his long legs slide into the aisle.

The Reverend opened his Bible and read, "Those who won't work should not eat." Then he added, "especially when there's an offer of work. All able bodied men better sign up with Mr. Collins or you'll have to move on. A man should earn his own way if he can." By the time the preacher got into his sermon, sweat poured down his pale face. Edward made a game of counting the drops that fell from the man's chin. When the final "Amen" was said, the preacher wiped his face with his shirt sleeve and retreated to the dining quarters in the back room. Row by row the congregation stepped into the aisle and followed him to the wooden tables for their evening meal. They stood until grace was said.

"Hurry and eat. Want to get outta this place," Coop told Jane. "Some smell like they ain't had a bath in a month." Edward gulped his food for he knew as soon as his father wanted to leave, the family would have to drop their forks and follow him.

"Guess there ain't nothin' to do but pick cotton," he announced leaving the hot building and stepping out into the cooler Autumn air. Edward squinted against the brilliant sun as he followed his father and mother to where Mr. Collins' spokesperson was leaning against a building smoking a cigarette.

"Me and this boy will pick," Coop bluntly stated.

"Edward is only a child!" Jane gasped. "He won't be able to pick cotton all day in the hot sun." Placing her hands on her stomach when the baby inside kicked, she continued, "Besides they won't let an eight-year-old work the fields." She pulled on Coop's shirt sleeve.

"Whatcha want?" he growled. She stepped backward out of his reach.

"I'll pick. Edward can watch the children at the edge of the field. Please, Coop?"

"You daft, woman?" he angrily faced her. "Whatcha think people would say 'bout me lettin' a pregnant woman pick cotton? Boy's big 'nuf to pick. It'll do him good." Turning back to the man he asked, "Where's these fields at?"

While Coop got directions from the man, Jane gently put her arm across Edward's thin shoulders and hugged him.

"I can do it," Edward grinned at his mother. Although only eight years old, his head already came to her shoulder. He glanced at his father for approval, but the look he got caused him to hang his head and scuff the toe of his shoe in the dirt.

"Don't be ruinin' them shoes, boy!"

14

"Yes, sir." He walked slowly behind his parents back to the Army Hall for a painful blister had formed where his heels slid in and out of the second hand shoes the Salvation Army had given him.

Excitement over working the next day kept Edward awake that night and the cardboard he lay on seemed unusually hard and uncomfortable. It wasn't until almost dawn that the boy finally drifted into light sleep.

****

Edward slung his shoes over his shoulder and walked in the grass next to the road when the family headed for the cotton fields. The oily smell of the tar mixed with the dusty morning heat made his stomach sick, but he didn't dare complain. After trudging out of the city and into the country, the cotton fields stretched before them like huge groups of fluffy white sheep.

"Looks like a boss man," Coop snarled. "You stay here 'til I see if'n Tubby over there works for Mr. Collins." Edward watched while his Pa stalked toward a heavy man standing beside a horse-drawn wagon under a lone shade tree. The boy snickered when the fat man spat a large glob of tobacco juice close to his Pa's feet.

"Watch where you're spittin'!" Coop yelled.

"Didn't hit yah did I?" the man replied with a chuckle.

"No, but damn close."

"Well then, no harm's done now is there?"

Because he couldn't hear what else was said, Edward turned his attention to workers tugging long sacks of cotton between the rows. The dark-skinned people straightened up every once in a while, placed their hands on their hips and stretched their backs before bending over to continue their work. The boy was beginning to think that his mother had been right when she said this was hard work. These people looked plumb tuckered out.

Edward was startled into action by his Pa's voice shouting "Come here, boy!"

"This here boy and me'll be pickin'," Coop stated while yanking on Edward's arm, drawing him closer to the boss man.

"Yo-all be able to pick cotton youngun?" the large man asked, swabbing rivulets of sweat from his pudgy red face.

"Course he can," Coop answered.

"Yo-all wants the boy to pick?" The man's tone made Coop set

15

his jaw and double his fist.

"Said we'd pick. We'll pick," Coop snarled.

"Names?" the man asked as he shrugged and pulled a pad of paper from the wagon.

"Cooper and Edward."

"He your son?"

Coop silently stared straight ahead with his mouth clamped shut while the boss man grabbed a bag from the wagon and threw it on the ground.

"Each bag made to hold 100 pound. We pay by bag full. Yo-all gets a place to stay long's yo-all work. Ain't the best. Good 'nuf for sheltah I reckon." Pointing a chubby finger toward a row of small shacks he said, "No. 3 is yourn long's yo-all work." Edward shielded his eyes from the sun glaring on the tin roofs and stared at the shacks with their rough board siding and windows with no covering.

"Boy's workin' too," Coop stated. "Don't forget that."

"Don't get yah any extree, 'cept 'nother bag," the man chortled as he threw down a second sack. "Soon's yo-all get settled in No. 3, start pickin'." He signaled them to follow him. "Show you No. 3." As Edward watched the boss man waddle along the path, he thought how much this man resembled Fat Jim back in Rhode Island. He hadn't thought there was another man as fat as him in all the world and here he was following a duplicate of Jim's fat behind down the path.

No. 3 was a small three room shack that smelled of dust, smoke and burned food. It stood in a row of shanties placed about 30 feet apart, facing another line of shacks. Both rows of houses opened onto the dirt pathway where a long hose lay, lazily trickling water for everyone to share. There was no electricity in No. 3. No screens or glass in the windows. A kerosene lamp sat on the table, its chimney blackened with soot. A layer of dust covered the meager furniture.

"You two go ahead to work," Jane said cheerfully waving them away. "I'll have this place cleaned up by the time you get back." Coop turned on his heels and started for the field with Edward running to keep up with him.

"We'll be needing kerosene!" Jane called after them.

"If'n they pay tonight I'll get some. Otherwise, we'll go without. You know I ain't got no money!" Coop angrily called over his shoulder.

****

16

A loop over Edward's shoulder held the long sack, leaving his hands free for picking cotton. The outer pods had split and dried making needle sharp prickles. These put painful scratches on the boy's hands as he pulled the fat white cotton bolls from their prickly pods. The scorching sun beat on his head and made him dizzy. He constantly changed positions to relieve his aching back and shoulders. Before the bag was half full, it dragged behind him like an anchor. Sweat ran down his face and dripped from his chin.

Slipping the loop off of his sunburned shoulder, he headed for the water bucket. After gulping a drink from the dipper, he dumped the rest of its contents over his head. He watched from the corner of his eye as his father tugged a bag of cotton to the boss. The man hoisted it onto a scale attached to the wagon and piled rocks on the opposite side until it balanced. Then he handed Coop a piece of paper.

"This here can be spent at company store today or turned in for cash money at end of the month," the boss said. Coop took the paper and stuck it in his shirt pocket before angrily turning to Edward.

"Whatcha standin' there for, boy. Get working! That watah's for drinkin', boy, not for bathin'!" he bellowed, giving Edward a swift kick to his backsides. "Now get back to work!" The workers stopped picking to see what the commotion was about. Thoroughly embarrassed, Edward grabbed the bag, ran to the field, placed the strap over his shoulder and started to pull. The bag wouldn't budge. Leaving it in the row, he gathered armfuls of cotton and ran back to stuff them into the bag. He backed away

cotton boll

when he saw his father coming toward him, fearful he would get another kick. Relief almost brought tears to his eyes when his father grabbed the bag and took it over to the wagon. The scale showed Edward had picked 70 pounds of cotton. He was elated, but his father wasn't satisfied.

"What's the mattah, boy? Put your mind to it. Shoulda had a full bag," Coop scolded as Edward hung his head. This humiliating day made him determined that tomorrow he would drag that cotton bag until it was full if it killed him.

The boss man wrote the weight on a chit and handed it to Coop who strode toward the Company Store which stood beside the line of shacks. The chits were turned in for a pint of kerosene and bread.

A weary, discouraged child fell asleep right after supper with an aching back and hands torn from cotton pods. He never woke as mosquitos flew in the open windows, buzzed around his head, filled themselves with his blood, and flew away--leaving red welts on his body.

After stooping and crawling down row upon endless row of cotton for a week, Edward was getting the hang of it, but he was grateful to the boss man for coming up with bags which held only 50 pounds. The sun bothered him less as his skin tanned chestnut brown. Another worker took pity on him and gave him a large brimmed hat. At the end of each day, he took pride that he had picked two bags full (100 pounds). The chits were taken to the company store where Coop bought himself a bottle of liquor to quench his thirst. What money was left was spent on food for the family. Edward stood before the candy case with its licorice whips, squirrel bars, hot balls, gum, nuts and other sweets and wished his father would give him a penny to spend but he didn't dare ask, and his father never offered to buy him any of the sweets.

****

"What's the mattah, Mama?" Edward called as he ran to where Jane lay moaning on the bed. He and his father had entered No. 3 to find no supper and Parnell and Laura sitting on the floor watching their mother with wide frightened eyes.

"Oh, Coop!" she screamed. "It's time!"

"Get outdoors, all of you!" Coop hollered as he shoved Edward aside and walked over and gently laid his hand on Jane's forehead. With a kindness in his voice that Edward had never heard before he whispered, "I'll be right back, Jane."

"Hurry!" Jane shrieked.

"Why is Mama crying?" Parnell bawled as he ran to his father and tried to grab his pant leg.

"Git away!" Coop shouted pushing Parnell aside. "Edward, get these kids outside!" Although the boy wished to stay with his mother, he obediently herded the other two children out of the shack and sat them under a shade tree where they huddled together and nervously listened to their mother's loud cries.

Coop returned with a stout woman dressed in white who militantly kept in stride beside him. They had been inside the shack only a short while when Coop came out and filled a couple of buckets with water.

"Is Mama goin' be a'right?" Parnell whimpered as he clung to Edward. "I'm 'fraid."

"She's all right," Edward reassured him. "She's havin' a baby. She'll stop screamin' soon. She's not dyin' or nothin'." Although he had never been allowed in the room when a baby was born, he remembered his mother explaining how Laura had come. He felt very grown up and important that he knew some things his younger brother and sister didn't know. He put his arms around them and the three children sat nestled together ... waiting.

Time dragged slowly and it seemed forever before the midwife came out and gave them permission to come inside.

"Got a new sister," she announced proudly as though she herself had produced the child. "Come on in." Edward ran to No. 3 with Parnell and Laura close behind. Crowding around their mother's bed they stared at the wrinkled red-faced baby that lay beside their mother.

"Whatcha gonna call her?" the midwife asked.

"Candice," Jane said without any hesitation. Then turning to her husband she weakly said, "Coop, give the children somethin' to eat and get them to bed, please." He grabbed half a loaf of bread off the table and shoved it toward Edward.

"Eat and git to bed."

"Yes, sir," Edward quickly replied. Smelling liquor on his father's breath and noting he was in a nervous agitation, the boy hurried the children off to the bedroom. After tearing off chunks of bread and gobbling them, they fell asleep on the mattress that kept them off the dirt floor.

****

While Jane was regaining her strength, Coop and Edward quit picking cotton and hired on to pick strawberries. The heat, dust and back-breaking work seemed worse each day as the boy crawled along the rows. The small shack they had fled from up north seemed like a palace compared to No. 3 and Edward thought every day about Rhode Island and his friend Floyd.

"Gettin' tired of workin' like a damn slave," Coop announced one day. "We're headin' north. Cain't no place on earth be wor'n this." The smile on Jane's face told Edward that she, too, had been waiting for

19

that decision. The next day Jane went to the Salvation Army and asked for help. A collection of $7.00 was taken up for the family--enough to pay some of the way on the train--but Coop chose to ride the boxcars instead.

"Why give away your money when we can ride for free?" he boasted.

"Coop, we don't even know where the trains are going," Jane objected.

"Goin' north. That's all we needs to know."

Edward was exhilarated over his father's decision to hop into boxcars bound for unknown places. It was like a vacation with nothing to do but ride the train every day and see what was at the next station.

The family hopped the first train headed in a northerly direction, but after a long ride up through Tennessee, they discovered they were in Chicago, Illinois, not much closer to Rhode Island than they had been in Alabama.

From Bread Lines to Hooversville

The thriving cities of 1929 were now feeling the full impact of the Depression. In Chicago Edward looked longingly at a crate of apples on the sidewalk with a crude cardboard sign tucked behind them that read "APPLES 10¢". A man in dirty torn overalls with two small girls clinging to his ragged shirt sleeves watched them as they got closer.

"Wish we could help those poor folk," Jane said sadly.

"Why should we? Just beggars. Don't even look at them," Coop growled.

"The children look so scrawny. Maybe we could buy just a couple of apples?" Jane ventured, but Coop continued to stare straight ahead ignoring her plea. Edward glanced at the two pitiful girls in over-sized tattered dresses. Their hair looked like their pa had chopped it off with a jackknife. Their pleading eyes stared up hopefully at Jane and Coop. The smallest girl clutched a one-legged doll that reminded Edward of the wooden train with missing wheel that he had played with when he had been five years old. He felt a surge of the same anger and frustration he had as a youngster when his father tripped over Parnell's truck and ended up angrily retaliating by burning Edward's precious wooden train in the cook stove.

"Please mister. Apple for a dime." The larger girl shyly held out an apple to Coop. She stumbled as he angrily shoved her out of the way. Quickly retrieving the apple from the sidewalk, she held it out to the next passerby. Noticing his mother's embarrassment, Edward slunk by the little group with his eyes intently staring at the sidewalk.

****

21

During the journey to and from Florida, the family's survival depended on the bread lines located in the poorer districts of the cities. The main dole from these lines was government surplus consisting of prunes, rice and grains. Whenever they headed for one of these long lines, Edward knew he was in for a stretch of standing and waiting. His stomach was used to very little food, but today he was thinking how good a chunk of meat would taste.

"How come there's no place 'round here where Pa can kill a deer?" he asked his mother remembering the stories his father told about jacking deer in the woods of Rhode Island. The meat from those animals had always tasted good the way his Mom cooked it.

"This is a city," Jane answered as she shifted Candice from one hip to the other. "There's building's all around us. Where yah suppose a deer would live?"

"I don't know, but why we standin' in line all the time?"

"Stop complaining, Edward," his mother said. "We have to stand in line if we want food to eat." Her voice sounded as irritated as Edward felt.

"Why can't we buy somethin' at the store?" he pouted.

"We have no money. Just be quiet," Jane responded. Edward hung his head and scuffed the dirt at his feet as he thought about the money the Salvation Army had given his Pa. Seven dollars seemed like a lot to him, but the only thing he had seen his father pay for was cigarette makings and liquor. He didn't dare look in his father's direction for fear he would get hollered at or hit, so he stood and passed the time by listening to the men jawing back and forth.

"Just a damn shame way gov'ment treats us," Coop complained. "Did yah hear 'bout the bastard in the White House lendin' money to farmers to buy seed. Lends them money to feed animals, but cares less that we ain't got a job."

"Right yah are," the man said. "Got any makin's on yah?"

"Only for myself," he replied as he tapped tobacco into a cigarette paper. Then grabbing the tag at the end of the string in his teeth, he pulled the pouch of Bull Durham closed and returned it to his shirt pocket with the string and tag dangling on the outside. Slowly rolling the fag he looked at the man who had asked for makin's with a sadistic smile and shining dark eyes. After licking the fag to stick the paper Coop gently ran his fingers up and down its length several times before lighting it, all the while staring at the man until he angrily stalked away further down the line, hoping to find a kinder soul. Coop grinned as he took a drag on the cigarette, slowly exhaling and watching the smoke spiral above his head.

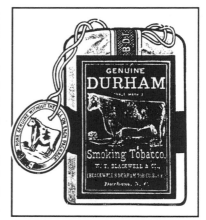

Bull Durham tobacco,
1 oz. for 5¢

"Come next election," another man behind Coop spoke up. "Hoover's out. That Roosevelt fella runnin' ag'in him has good ideas."

"Think he'd care about us?" another man sneered.

"Figure he's what this country needs. By golly I'd vote for him."

Edward stepped forward another two feet as the line moved. Awkwardly standing on one foot and then the other like a heron in a pond, he tried to get relief for his tired feet. The soles of his shoes were so thin that the bottoms of his feet had become bruised from stepping on pebbles.

The whole family was glad when they got to the head of the line and received their free food. Hurrying to the cool shade of a little park nearby, Coop and Jane sat under a shade tree with the baby while the other children ran barefoot through the grass, exploring the area.

Edward was intrigued by a row of make-shift shacks surrounded by hard-packed dirt where the grass had been worn away by many feet. These crude buildings leaned against each other at strange angles like tree houses made by children. He slowly walked toward them.

"Whatcha got there?" he asked a small black boy who was struggling toward the shanties carrying a bucket.

"Wattah," he replied in a barely audible voice.

"Want me to help yah?" Edward asked, reaching for the handle.

"Naw," the boy replied, pulling the heavy container closer to him. The bucket whacked his skinny legs as he walked, splashing water onto the dusty ground that left a wobbly dark trail behind him.

"I's livin' here," the boy said, stopping in front of a rough doorway.

Edward stared at the small building constructed of wood, metal and cardboard, squinting to try and see if people truly lived inside.

A quick glance toward where his mother and father were sitting with their backs to him gave Edward confidence they hadn't noticed he was talking to a black boy so he asked, "Can I come in?" The adventure of going where he knew his father would not want him to go plus his inquisitive nature made him want to see all the more what was inside the darkened interior. The small boy shrugged and Edward took that for a "Yes." Stooping down, he followed the boy through the low doorway where he stood silently waiting while his eyes adjusted to the darkness. Two automobile seats against opposite walls, a small sterno stove sitting on a crate at the end of the room, and a couple of cardboard boxes made up the furnishings. A colorful blanket was drawn smoothly over one seat. A thin black woman occupied the other.

"That your mama?" Edward whispered to the boy.

"Yah-sah."

"Howdy," the woman smiled, displaying large white teeth. "Yo-all gonna stay here in Hoovasville?" she asked. Before Edward could answer, she continued, "Guess yo-all met Joey. He's such a good boy." She reached over and hugged the small child. "Did yo-all be livin' in Hoovasville, did yah say?"

"Don't know where Hoovasville is at," Edward answered.

"Well, I nevah!" the woman laughed. "Boy, yo-all be standin' in Hoovasville."

"My Pa said we're in Chicago. Ain't that where we're at?"

"Why," she laughed again, "this be Chicago all right. We named these buildin's we's in Hoovasville."

"Why'd yah do that?"

"Named it aftah Pres'dent of this United States. His last name be Hoovah. Heard tell of him, boy?"

"My Pa don't like him!" Edward blurted out.

"He'd be strange if'n he did," the woman said. "Pres'dent livin' in big white house, supposin' to take care of the people, but he's an insult to God and this country."

Edward couldn't understand the ramblings of the woman. He realized she was as bitter against this Hoover fellow as his father was and decided to change the subject onto a happier note.

"We just got to Chicago on a train. Got some food and we're

24

headin' back to Rhode Island," Edward commented.

"Well, God bless yo-all on yah journey, young'un." Edward felt awkward standing and watching the small boy holding fast to his mother and noisily sucking his thumb.

"Uh ... you sleep here?" Edward asked the woman, pointing to the automobile seat with the blanket.

"Sho 'nuf. Hafta."

"I like these seats," Edward said, running his hand over the covering on the back of the seat. The seats were longer and wider than any he had seen and felt smooth like leather; not at all scratchy like the seats that he had endured on his ride to Florida in the Model T. "Where'd yah get these seats? Did yah lose your car? We lost ours in the ocean in Florida."

"We nevah had no car. Seats come from junk yard yondah." The woman pointed off into space. "My husban' drug them outta fancy car. Can't rightly tell yo-all what kine, but we's thankin' the good Lord for them for they keeps us off'n the groun'."

"I gotta go," Edward unceremoniously announced. Bolting into the sunshine, he ran toward the trees, anxious to tell his mother about the strange little houses and the people who lived in them. His excitement was short-lived for his father intercepted him, grabbing him by the arm and angrily staring at him.

"Damn good thing yah got yourself back here!" his father yelled. "We're ready to eat and you're runnin' 'round with some nigger kid!"

"But, Sir, I saw ... "

"Don't care what yah saw!" he screamed. Edward fell backwards from a slap across his face and found himself sprawled on the ground. "You're gonna get more than a slap if'n yah ever take up with niggers ag'in. You're no son of mine, takin' up with trash. Now eat your suppah!" His father strode out of sight behind the trees while Edward slowly sat up. Munching his supper of bread and dried prunes, he stared at Hooversville. His father's hatred for these folks thoroughly confused him.

"Edward!" his mother called from the duck pond. "Finish eating and come get cleaned up!" Parnell laughed and his sisters squealed with delight as Edward ran and jumped into the pond, splashing them with lukewarm water. Ducks flapped their wings and quacked noisily at these intruders, all the while staying out of reach of the noisy children that were trying to catch them.

"Why does Pa talk bad 'bout black folks?" Edward asked Jane. He had seen his father in a white hooded KKK outfit and heard the bad things he and other men said about black people, but did not understand why they had such hatred.

"He just doesn't care for them," she whispered, looking nervously in Coop's direction.

"Why? They ain't bad." Talking rapidly, he told his mother about Hooversville and the small black boy and his friendly mother who lived in a strange little building.

"Don't mention any of this in front of your father," she scolded him. "Don't cause trouble, Edward."

"All right," he said. Sullenly he followed his mother back to where Coop was impatiently standing with his hands on his hips.

"I'm ready to leave," Coop announced turning and hastily heading across the park. Jane grabbed the small children and struggled to keep Coop in sight. They caught up with him when they reached the rail yard where they hopped another freight and the next leg of their journey back to Rhode Island was begun.

> *"Then followed a succession of lifts, sometimes by a kindly motorist, sometimes on a freight train, as the first stage of their exodus had been made."*
> *[Providence Journal, November 16, 1930]*

The first and only time Coop paid actual cash for the family was in Baltimore. He hired a jitney for 35 cents to take them outside the city limits. Further along, two traveling salesmen took pity on the family of hitchhikers and squeezed them into the bed of the open depot hack where they bounced uncomfortably on a bed of hay. After a day and a half of traveling they arrived in Woonsocket, Rhode Island on October 12.

> *"With only $3 in his pocket, [Coop's] family spent the night in the police station. The Woonsocket police as their contribution to the great heartedness of America took up a collection for them; not only that but put them in a machine and drove them all the way to East Greenwich."*

Back in Rhode Island the family took up where they had left off three years before. They settled into another cheap rental and Coop reluctantly went out to find work.

Edward was eight years old when he finally started his education in the one-room schoolhouse with smaller and younger children who looked up to this tall first grader. Although awkward and shy, he was eager to learn and quickly caught up with the other children his age. After completing the fourth grade, he was taken out of school to help support the family.

The family squeezed into the bed of the open depot hack where they bounced uncomfortably on a bed of hay.

"Crazy Coop"

Tension in the small kitchen was suffocating. Edward felt it filling the room like a living, breathing thing that pressed his guts and made his insides ache. Although six people were seated around the cracked wooden table, the only noises were the steady ticking of the clock on the wall and an occasional grating of a fork against a plate. The fourteen year old boy had been extremely hungry after working on the hay wagon at Mr. Johnson's farm all day. But now the food had no appeal for him. The kitchen smelled of burned onions and wood smoke that made his sinuses run. Hunching over, he stared at his supper of fried potatoes and blackened onions that lay in a greasy pile on his plate. Although he had eaten nothing but three biscuits for lunch, a queasiness in his stomach made him feel like throwing up.

As Edward did so often lately, he retreated into the solace of his imagination in order to escape his surroundings. He stared at his plate with such intensity that his mind completely shut out the people about him. Dragging the tines of his fork through the potatoes, he formed what looked like a railroad track. In his mind he relived the accidental meeting he had with his friend Floyd at the rail yard that afternoon.

"Will you be coming back to school this fall do you think?" Floyd had asked as they sat on the grassy hill overlooking the tracks. Edward still remembered the blood rushing to his face and the muscles in his stomach tightening into a cramp. He had lashed out at his friend.

"No! I work, remember?! I don't need any more schoolin'. Boy, what a stupid question!" He was sorry the minute he'd said it, but words once said were said forever.

"I'm sorry, Ed," Floyd said with his voice cracking. "I wasn't meaning to upset you. It's just that I miss you at school."

28

"Well, I ain't goin' back." Edward's eyes had filled with tears as he turned away from Floyd. He ached just thinking that he would never go to school again.

The two boys had sat staring silently at the powerful trains stretched out on the tracks, slowly puffing black smoke and cinders into the air until the lengthening shadows reached out from the trees and folded over the tracks. Edward still remembered the lump in his throat when he brushed the dirt and grass from his clothes and, without another word, headed out.

He was in bad humor all the way home for he felt like his Pa was taking advantage of him by demanding his full paycheck each week. In spite of his help the family still moved from house to house every few months because his Pa wouldn't or couldn't pay the rent. He hated his father just as he hated this silence around him.

Brought back to reality by a strange feeling that he was being observed, Edward glanced up and gazed into his father's scrutinizing deepset eyes. Coop was squinting at him from under dark protruding eyebrows. The boy quickly lowered his head turning his attention back to his plate. Chair legs creaked loudly as his father shifted his postion, all the while scraping noisily at his plate. The annoyance of his father had the same effect on Edward that a bolt of lightning would have had if it had struck the room. It immobilized him and made his head hurt. He tried to figure out what was wrong with his Pa but it only gave him more of a headache. Oh, to hell with him. What did he care what bothered the man anyway? He wished Coop was not his father. Even homeless hoboes riding the highballing trains must be happier than anyone in this house. He envied the two men he and Floyd had seen that afternoon standing in the open door of a boxcar, waving to the boys until the train was out of sight. He longed to be free like those men instead of squeezed into this small house where people didn't dare speak or move.

Uncertainty as to how his father would react kept Edward from sprinting outside to breathe; to hear animals, peep frogs, wind sighing through swaying trees--just any noise at all that would stop the continuous tick-tick-tick of the clock as it struck blow after blow to his brain. Turning his head slightly he sneaked a look at his father. How disgusting, he thought, as food slopped onto the table from the jerky motions of the intoxicated man stabbing and scraping at his plate. What

29

a drunken fool. It's no wonder everyone in town calls him "Crazy Coop." I just wish he'd drop dead and get out of my life.

A terrible fear took hold of Edward. His father was staring at him through blood-shot eyes. Suppose his father could read his thoughts? He bowed his head and nervously thrust his fork into a piece of potato. Before he could get it to his mouth, there was a quick half-shaking, half-twitching movement from the tall man. This movement intensified the anxiety in the boy causing him to drop the fork back onto his plate.

"More!" The sudden roar shattered the silence like the clashing of cymbals. Five pairs of frightened eyes turned toward Coop as though they had been choreographed. Edward's heart raced. He quietly drew deep breaths and slid his chair further away from his father, just in case he decided to strike him. The younger children shifted nervously in their chairs. Unaffected by the children's reactions, Coop shoved his plate toward Jane. Her hand shook as she gently removed it from her husband's unsteady grip. Edward saw the hopelessness in his mother's eyes. Her features looked pinched, so that the 37-year-old woman looked to be about 50. Her voice whined as she apologized, "I'm sorry, Coop, there is no more."

"Sorry! That's all you can say is sorry! Hell, you're always sorry!" he shouted thrusting his face close to hers and belching loudly. Jane recoiled at the stench of liquor on his breath. "Sorry excuse for a suppah, sorry excuse for a wife ...sorry, s o r r y ... Coop's voice trailed off. His chin drooped and rested on his chest. Edward hoped Pa would sleep the rest of the night; or, if he were dead, that would be even better. But the all too few minutes of relief were abruptly ended by a rough barking noise from deep in Coop's throat. His face contorted into a silly grin. His head and neck extended like a snake ready to strike. The fleeting senseless appearance of his Pa suddenly turned into a frightening image. While frowning, he screwed up his eyes and stared at Edward with disgust. He _is_ loony. Floyd was right when he said the folks in town call my Pa "Crazy Coop" Edward thought. The tolerable side of Pa was seen less frequently the older he got. He had always been strict and unreasonable with people when sober, but irrational, stupid and hateful when he had been drinking, which lately was most of the time. He was an absurd madman when liquor took hold of him and Edward was wise enough to keep out of his way. At times like this, no one knew what to say or how to react.

"Damn!" Coop growled. Jumping to his feet, he staggered backwards, almost falling to the floor. A solid kick with his boot sent a chair crashing into the counter behind him. He steadied himself by placing both palms on the table while Jane cringed back against the sink. Although violence in the household was nothing new to Edward, he never got used to it. In an effort to prevent his mother from being struck by his Pa, Edward said, "You may have mine. I'm not hungry anyway." He cautiously held out his plate to the man.

"Damn you, boy!" I ain't eatin' your garbage!" The drunken man smashed his ungrateful hand into the center of the extended offering. The plate shattered into pieces of colorful bits of porcelain which mingled with fried potatoes and greasy blackened onions that landed with a plop onto the linoleum. The tall man's eyes looked steadily at Edward through dark wavy hair hanging limply across his face.

"You miserable pup. How yah s'posed to talk to me?" Coop's words slurred slowly in rhythm with his swaying body. Edward knew his father expected him to say something, but his brain was frozen and he sat mutely staring at the man. His mother leaned over and whispered, "Call your father *Sir.*"

"Sir, you may have mine, *Sir."* *Sir* was articulated slowly and clearly but the boy's mind was not in a respectful mood. Who the hell does he think he is? The drunken fool can make me call him sir, but he sure can't read my thoughts, else'n he'd kill me dead. Edward's eyes were expressionless as he tried to shut out the ugly scene and the man who he called Pa. Clamping his jaws tight kept his thoughts from tumbling out of his mouth, for he knew if he said another word it would mean trouble for the whole family. Gently touching his mother's shoulder as he passed, he bent down for the cleaning pail and rag. All was silent again except for the clink of the pail set into the black iron sink and the squeak of the pump handle. Soon, a thunderous splash of cold water flooded into the metal pail. Another vigorous pump and the pail was half full. Edward noislessly lifted it to the floor and started cleaning up the mess on the linoleum, working dangerously close to his father's feet.

"Down on your knees scrubbin' where yah belong boy! Clumsy ass!" Edward comforted himself with thoughts that his father might

31

try to kick him. Then he could grab the man's ankle and send him flying. Being drunk, he'd hit the floor for sure. It'd serve him right too. In spite of these wishes, he doubted he would have the courage to do anything like that to his Pa. Instead, he meekly tried to defend himself with words.

"I only offered you my supper, *Sir.*" Noting that sarcasm had crept into the boy's voice, Jane shushed him.

"If it weren't for you brats there'd be food for a workin' man. Yah all take ... take ... take ... the whole lot of yah." Coop babbled on, his arms swinging in an arc of exaggerated gestures as he pointed at the cowering children.

"Coop, you aren't being fair." The tremor in Jane's voice made Edward wish his mother wouldn't try to reason with the man. Her eyes were like a frightened trapped animal as she faced her husband and continued. "The children never complain about what they don't have. Edward does a man's job and you get his whole paycheck. He works hard and many days without any lunch." Jane might as well have been talking to a stone, for Edward could see his father from the corner of his eye. The man showed no reaction to his wife's comments. His attention had been constantly directed to Edward trying to get grease off the linoleum with cold water and a rag. Shaking his finger at the boy, he shouted, "I saw yah hangin' 'round railroad tracks today ... watchin' worthless bums. You and that stupid Floyd. Wastin' time. Neither one of yah worth a good fart!"

Leaning back in his chair, Coop stretched his legs as Jane came near the table causing her to stumble over them and crash into the counter. Coop snickered. In his drunken state he was oblivious to the tears that glistened in her eyes.

"I asked yah a question, boy," he said, pulling his legs back and straightening up. Edward shook nervously as his father yelled, "Didn't yah hear?! Yah deaf as well as stupid?!"

Although he had heard no question among the man's ramblings, Edward answered, "Yes sir, I heard you." Then he fled from the room, leaving the bucket and rag on the floor.

Lying on his bed, he covered his head with the blanket and tried to shut out his father's ravings and the terrible guilt he felt for the hateful thoughts he entertained. His stomach rumbled from hunger and his head ached with fear that maybe *he was* the cause of his father's anger and beatings. "Life stinks!" he said aloud, as a hopelessness consumed him. Depressing thoughts filled his mind. He would never go back to school and be with his friends again. His dismal future was that of working in the woods with a man he despised and feared. He was good for nothing but to work. Feeling like a stranger instead of a member of the family, how he wished he could shake the family from his head like a dog shakes water from its hair. Maybe the two men riding the boxcar and waving at him and Floyd from the train were shaking themselves loose from their hard times. He envied them their freedom. Fighting his sorrow as long as he could, he finally gave in to the weight of depression. Sobs convulsed his body until he fell asleep, exhausted.

He dreamed he was watching his father from the open door of a boxcar. No matter how fast his Pa ran, the man could not catch the train. His silhouette grew smaller and smaller until he could no longer be seen. At least in his dream, Edward was free from his father's tyranny.

Confrontation

Edward's muscles had hardened from pulling a cross-cut saw and dragging limbs and tree trunks in the woods for a year. Although only fifteen years old, he was now wiry and as tall as his father. Each week he became more and more reluctant to give his unopened check to help support the family. Every payday he thought about keeping some money for himself, but always crumbled under the dark piercing eyes of his father.

Wind penetrated his thin jacket causing him to draw his arms closer to his slender body. Fumbling inside his jacket pocket, he felt the envelope containing his pay check. He hurried because he had stayed too long watching the trains being loaded and unloaded at the freight yards. His mind was filled lately with the magnetism of these powerful trains with their wheels as high as a man was tall. He fantasized that he would one day gain his freedom by riding out of town on one of them. Automatically he checked his pocket for the tenth time to reassure himself that his pay was still there.

It was October, but the beauty of the foliage with its brilliant reds and yellows went unnoticed. The cool breeze picked the brightly colored leaves from the trees, gently depositing them on top of the damp, rotted mulch from previous years. As Edward hustled through the ankle-deep carpet of brittle leaves he thought he heard a voice call. "Hurry, boy! Hurry, boy!" Startled, he cautiously looked up and down the dirt driveway to see where the person was who called. The woods were alive with activity here in East Greenwich, but he was the only human being in sight. He was a lonely boy trudging toward a home he detested, hearing commands sounding inside his head.

A squirrel, cheeks bulging with acorns, crossed his path and scampered up a maple tree. A flock of geese honked loudly overhead

34

as they headed for the pond where they would stay the night. A deer surprised Edward as it crashed through the underbrush. With white tail held high, it disappeared into the trees on the other side of the road.

Edward, too, was a frightened animal, hurrying to a place where he could spend the night, but knew his home had no safety or freedom for him. He thought of his home as a prison with his father the jailer. Hatred festered into a full fledged rage. His mind was filled with long dark shadows even more dense than the black patches covering his pathway and hiding the beauty of the sinking sun. He strode rapidly as he thought about Pa waiting for the paycheck.

Seeing the outline of a small, flimsy-walled shack coming into view, the tired, hungry, angry fifteen-year-old slouched along hoping his father was not at home. Edward could hardly bear seeing his mother with black eyes, split lips, and bruises on her arms. These physical outbursts from his father against his mother had seemed to be more frequent lately and part of the everday life of the household . Edward and the other children were emotionally and physically caught in the middle of these struggles.

Edward's insides constricted every time he recalled the night a year ago when he had lain awake listening to his father and mother fighting. That fateful night it was decided Edward would go to work for the lumber company. For a year now he had brought his paycheck home each week and handed it to his father unopened. It was only recently that he had been given the change from his check for spending money. This only happened because he had found his Pa sober one day and had gotten up enough courage to ask for $3.00 a week to spend on a movie or something for himself.

He could still hear his father's reply. "What's a stupid kid gonna do with money anyway? Furnish yah a roof over your head 'n' food on the table. Oughta be grateful for that 'stead of comin' 'round askin' for money."

"Coop, why don't you give the boy a little money? We can tighten up a bit," his mother had pleaded on his behalf. His father had sat silently glaring at his wife before he spoke.

"Okay, boy, you can have whatever change is in your pay each week." Probably about two cents Edward had thought.

"I was thinkin' of 'bout three dollars," Edward replied.

"You'll take the change and like it. Hear?"

"Yes, sir," Edward said for he knew there was no use in arguing. Although he hadn't said any more to his father, working weekly for a miserly few cents irked Edward tremendously, but fear of his father was stronger than his distress. He just endured, feeling as though life had indeed dealt him a bitter blow when it made Coop his Pa.

Now it was Autumn, the time when boys went back to school. He seldom saw his friend Floyd anymore. Getting closer to home, Edward's intense loneliness and discouragement became master of his body. Frustrated, he threw stones and acorns at the trees in uncontrollable anger. "Boy, get some water!" Plunk! Another stone hit a tree. "Worthless boy, take care of the mule!" A handful of acorns clattered as he hurled them onto the road in front of him. "Hand it over! Give me the pay check!" he screamed. "Stupid ass, do this - do that!" His father's constant demands filled him with a madness that boiled over into these fits of fury.

An image of his father emerged in his mind. A tall gaunt man, who seldom smiled. His sunken features reminded Edward of an Indian ready to go on the warpath. Dark black orbs were set into his tanned stony face. Outstanding eyebrows jutted slightly above these dark eyes.

"I hate my old man!" Edward cried out to the crow in the top of the big pine.

"Caw! Caw!" came the answer.

"Stupid crow! Whatcha care anyhow! You got your freedom. Fly where you want and do what you want."

He looked up into the trees and past their half-naked limbs into the darkening sky. "Why was I born into this family anyway?" If there was a God up there, he wished He would give him an answer. A fat gray squirrel chattered at him, scolding the boy for his intrusion into its world. "Oh, shut up, you fat ball of Fur!" Edward shouted. "What yah know anyway?"

Edward was close enough to the house now to hear the loud voice of his father, words slurred from too much alcohol.

"Where's that no-good idiot son of yours with his pay?!"

Hollering at Mom again, Edward thought. He forced his feet to keep moving toward the ever-increasing clamor, for his first instinct was to run and hide from confrontations. He wished he hadn't watched the trains so long for his mother was taking abuse from his father

36

because of it.

The continued bellowing from his father was now mingled with the baby's crying. In his mind, Edward could picture the terrified children, hiding -- peering out with frightened eyes from behind a chair or from under the table.

Ear-piercing screams filled the air and instinctively Edward knew his father was beating up on his mother. Years of frustration and hatred mushroomed, filling his body and erupting inside him like a volcano. He ran, chest heaving, heart pounding, and legs straining; bounding the distance like a deer in flight. Flinging the kitchen door open, he sprang beside his mother and stood facing his father with clenched fists.

"I hate you!" he screamed. "Leave my mother alone, you crazy drunk!" Hysterically words flew from his mouth and spewed into the room, uncontrolled. "I hate your guts! I'm tired of taking your crap!" They stood there, a father and son with eyes locked in hatred.

Jane groaned as she wrapped her arms tightly around her waist. "Please sit down and eat supper," she sobbed. Ignoring her, Coop squinted at Edward with dark glistening eyes. Edward knew he had crossed the line of no return, so he bravely stood his ground. His chest heaved with labored breathing as he waited for his father's next move.

"You bastard!" Coop roared. With lightning speed he struck Edward across the mouth. The boy could feel the warm blood running over his split lip and down his chin. Falling backwards onto the floor, his head and back collided with the kitchen cabinet. There was no physical pain for he was as drunk with hatred as his father was with alcohol. His nimble body coiled like a snake. Leaping to his feet, he struck his father a blow to the stomach. Coop bent over slightly and came up with his arm, walloping the boy on the chin with his fist. Edward grabbed the back of a kitchen chair to steady himself for everything in the room looked gray and blurred.

"I'll kill you! Damn brat!" His father swayed back and forth as he yelled.

"Please, Coop, stop!" Jane begged as she held onto her husband's arm with both hands. "Edward doesn't mean it. He's just trying to protect me." With a disgusted look, Coop raised his arm, releasing her grip as easily as a dog would shake a rag.

Jane reached for the sewing machine belt hanging by the door, but she was knocked aside by Coop as he yanked the belt from the hook.

Although Edward had developed muscles working in the woods, he was no match against the wiry older man who was used to -- and enjoyed fighting. Blow after blow with the belt struck the boy's midriff and back as he clung tightly to the chair. Keeping his teeth clenched, he kept groans from escaping his battered body. Edward knew there was no one to help him, for Jane had retreated to a corner with the children where they watched in horror. This was his fight and he had to do what he could to defend himself.

Edward tightened his hold on the back of the chair and lifted it above his head. "Damn you to hell!" he bawled as he swung the chair sideways, striking his father with such force that it broke and was wrenched from his hands, leaving him weak and shaken. Falling to the floor, he lay trembling with his arms wrapped around his head. With a final kick of his boot to Edward's ribs, Coop threatened, "You raise your hand to me ag'in, boy, and you'll be dead. I'll kill yah dead! Now git to the chores!"

Edward crawled toward the door, bruised and battered. Pulling himself up by the doorknob, he stood for a few seconds until the dizziness went away. Then, conscious of his mother's pleading and crying in the background, he fled from his father's presence. "Double damn you to hell!" he murmured.

Feeling was coming back into his shocked body, but he ignored the pain. His conscious bitterness against his father was a feeling greater than physical pain. This showdown had been a while in coming, but Edward took satisfaction remembering the look of surprise and hatred on his Pa's face. The father-son relationship had been rocky at best, but now lay broken, leaving an open wound on Edward's heart.

Oscar the mule galloped over and tried to force his head into the pail of grain.

"Back, Oscar!" Edward cried as he shoved the animal with his arm. He hardly noticed the pain that shot from his wounded wrist into his back and shoulder because hatred for his father still filled him with an inner numbness. After finishing the chores, he stalked defiantly into the house.

"Are you all right, Edward?" His mother's concern for him was comforting. "I'm so sorry," she whimpered. He smiled sympathetically at her as he looked into her puffy red eyes.

"I see the old man went to sleep," he remarked as he glanced with disgust at his father who was sleeping on the couch and snoring with his mouth open.

"Yes, he's asleep and for your sake I hope he stays that way. Here, sit down so I can put ointment on your cut," she said, gently wiping the blood off his mouth and chin with warm water.

"Chores are done," he said starting for the stairs.

"I saved your supper," his mother added quickly, removing a plate of food from the oven.

"Thank you, Mom." He sat stiffly in the chair chewing and swallowing what was on the plate without tasting what he was eating for his eyes were glued on Coop.

"Why do you let him treat you so mean?" he asked.

"I have no place to go," she said softly. " He does work. We have food on the table. You shouldn't aggravate him, Edward. As you get older, you'll make a life of your own."

"Well, I ain't takin' it forever!" he snapped. After one more look at his father, he went to his room in the attic. In the silence of the hot, stuffy room under the eaves, the exasperated boy let the tears flow until he had no more strength. He slept fitfully throughout the long night for his bruises hurt whichever way he turned. The creaking of shrinking boards in the night air were suspiciously taken as his father's footsteps coming to carry out his threat of killing him. He knew his father was capable of such violence and it frightened him.

****

When the blackness of night slowly turned to the full gray of morning, Edward stealthily tip-toed to the drawer and fumbled among his meager belongings. A bedroll was made by wrapping an extra set of clothes and a tin cup inside his blanket. A light rope tied at each end of the roll made it easy to carry over his shoulder. Cautiously he felt his way down the stairs and into the kitchen. Coop was still asleep on the couch in the living room as Edward took one more glance at the home he was leaving. Grabbing two biscuits from the table, he stuffed them into his pocket, hoping all the while that they were the old man's breakfast.

Carefully opening the creaking door, he stepped out into the frigid morning air and headed for the cover of the woods. He felt free. Without a moment's hesitation, he ran down the driveway toward the

39

freight yard where he could put distance between himself and his father. A train whistle blew a long lonely blast somewhere out in the countryside. That whistle sent a thrill up his spine. His arms covered with goose bumps. It was calling to him. This was the beginning of many whistle calls he would follow during the next months. He was determined to face what lay ahead, for nothing could persuade him to go back into that house.

by Alex Burns, 1994

PART II
RIDING THE RAILS

A New Identity

In the early morning gloom, obscure and frightening shapes appeared like black phantoms ready to attack him. The driveway had become a scary dark tunnel made by large overhanging branches. Edward's heart felt like it had become a caged wild animal slamming against his ribs, trying to get out of his body. Clinging to the bedroll on his shoulder, he hurried down the center of the dirt road. To assure himself there was nothing to be afraid of, he tried to whistle. A slight shrill blast was all that escaped his shaking, distorted lips.

Whoo! Whoo! An owl's hoot overhead startled Edward. Flapping its long wings, it glided silently to the safety of the forest. Edward sprinted down the driveway, covering a mile or more before the sun was up.

Slumping down beside the road, he gulped deep breaths. As soon as his body stopped shaking, he reached into his jacket pocket and took out the two biscuits he had grabbed from the kitchen. Eating slowly, he tried to figure whether he had made a mistake by leaving home. Despite the fact that he was glad to be away from his father, he wondered if he had left his mother in a worse predicament; but in the end, he was convinced life would be better for everyone without him around. His stiff aching body reminded him of the beating he had taken the night before. Pride wouldn't let him go back home even if he wanted, so he felt he better get down the road. He had made a decision. When a person runs away, it's for good and final and that was that.

A long shrill whistle signaled the arrival of the morning freight train. The sound drew Edward like a magnet. Slinging his bedroll over his shoulder, he raced in the direction of the rail yard.

Edward cautiously approached the tracks. He swallowed hard and fought back tears when he reached the small hill where he and Floyd had sat together so many times. Wonder what people will say when they hear I run away, he thought. Floyd would understand for he was the only one the boy had confided in. He was the only one that Edward would truly miss. "Bye, Floyd. See yah later," Edward said as he continued on over the hill.

From his vantage point he could see the tracks and the surrounding area. In a small ravine, hidden from the railroad police by trees and brush were three men. Thin wisps of light smoke and red sparks drifted up from the ground as they kicked dirt onto the fire to put it out. Three stones formed a small circle that had held an old coffee pot over the flame.

"Damn!" one man yelled as he snatched the handle of the pot and flung it aside.

"Hey, Rod, why don't yah grab it ag'in? Mighta cooled off by now!" one teased.

"You stupid ass," another said as he shook his head. "Don't be a hollerin' like that. Police gonna hear."

Edward approached the men from behind the brush and peered past them to the rail yard. One freight quietly puffed small black whiffs from its stack while its cargo was being unloaded. The other train was a giant coal-black engine sitting on the parallel track with a line of boxcars attached to it. Clouds of white steam hissed from its boiler into the clear Autumn air. Black smoke puffed from its stack. Edward's imagination came to life. The train was a friendly fire-breathing dragon with a head made from sweaty hot pieces of metal. The dragon's body was the line of dusty wooden cars. I'm gonna ride that old dragon he thought. That's my way out of this town. Gotta get into one of the boxcars without being seen. Wouldn't that be something if'n I ended up in jail and had to have my Pa come to the station to take me home. Even the thought made him shiver. Getting another beating with the sewing machine strap was enough incentive to reenforce his decision to get out of this place.

The man who had been called Rod turned and watched Edward's approach. Scratching his stubby beard, he cocked his head and scrutinized the boy. Then he bent and without a word picked up his bedroll and slung it over his shoulder. Leathery creases spread across his tanned forehead and around his blue-green eyes as he smiled at Edward. He looked middle-aged. His ragged overalls were decorated with many safety pins and buttons haphazardly clinging to its bib. When he raised his hand in welcome, Edward noticed a bright red stripe across his palm.

"Sorry 'bout your hand, man," Edward said. "And the coffee pot and all." The older man with graying whiskers snorted, shaking his head as he pointed a grimy finger at Rod.

"That's 'nuf, Whiskas!" Rod raised his voice sternly. The older man stopped chuckling at once and turned his back to watch the trains.

Rod stared at Edward's bruised face, "Looks like you had a fight with a wild cat."

"Might say that." Edward didn't pursue the conversation. There was no point in trusting Rod or Whiskas with any details of his life. They could be secret agents for the railroad for all he knew.

"Well, long's them bruises don't keep yah from grabbin' the laddah to a boxcar, yo-all will be okay," Rod drawled.

Edward tried to be cautious while he looked again at Rod's collection of safety pins and campaign and advertising buttons. He thought it a rather strange collection but reckoned a man was entitled to wear what he wanted. "Nice collection of pins," he remarked.

"Hobby with me." Rod smiled as he fingered the pins and buttons.

"Yeah. Maybe he'll need a hundred pins one day." Whiskas turned around and grinned again. Several of his front teeth were rotting out of his head. This fact, coupled with the gray beard, gave an impression that he was very old to be riding the trains. He looked older than dirt. He was wearing a suit several sizes too large for his skinny frame. The pants legs were folded up but still dragged behind him on the ground. Small twigs and leaves stuck out from his matted hair like an abandoned bird's nest. He studied Edward through dark rimmed glasses held together with tape at the nose piece and on the bow.

"Bettah wear your hat today," Rod chided Whiskas, like he was talking to his child. "Goin' be cool" Whiskas immediately took a corduroy cap from his jacket pocket. Pulling it firmly down over his matted hair, he secured the ear flaps by tying the strings under his chin.

"Now, yo-all lookin' good, Whiskas," Rod drawled with a wink at Edward. "Best be careful, old man, when yo-all catch the train. Those raggedy baggedy pants li'ble to catch on somethin' and get ripped

Whiskas looked like he had been homeless forever.

off'n your hide." Rod threw his head back and guffawed. The laugh lines around his eyes became deeper as he continued, "Sure'd be a sight --skinny ol' behin' showin' to the whole world as the train flies by." Edward was beginning to feel at ease with these two men.

The third man had ignored them all this time. He stood apart from the others and studied the trains. Perhaps it was his black skin that separated him from the others, Edward thought. Maybe Rod and Whiskas were prejudiced like Pa.

"What's your handle, boy?" Whiskas asked Edward.

"My handle?" he replied blankly.

"What be your name? What does people call yah?" The aggravation in Whiskas' tone made Edward feel stupid. He didn't answer right away for his brain was all muddled up. He couldn't give these strangers his name. Suppose one of them knew his Pa? He had to give them some answer for they were staring at him, waiting. He looked toward the ground. Remembering that his third grade teacher had informed him that probably his ancestors came from Scotland gave him an idea.

"My name is Scottie, sir," he said raising his head and looking Whiskas straight in the eyes. Whiskas looked quizzically at Rod and grinned. Scottie imagined they were laughing at the name he gave, but he couldn't see any joke in that. His face flushed with anger. Whiskas took off his glasses and wiped them on the lining of his suit coat as tears filled his eyes.

"Well now, Scottie, I ain't no *Sir*." he blurted out. "Look at us. All of us. We're just plain wanderers -- hoboes -- bums -- nothing more and nothing less. Guess you been raised with mannas, but just be callin' us Whiskas and Rod will do fine. Sorry if I offended yah, but I just ain't met a gaycat* for a while. Showin' respect to me tickled me 'bout into bustin' a gut." Now that Edward knew why they were laughing, he relaxed and studied the two men more closely. These men didn't want or need respect. They were content with what they were. It pleased him that they hadn't questioned his name. Now he had a new name of his own choosing. Never again would he be called Edward. He was *Scottie* -- a hobo -- who was about to ride the rails.

The black man crouched down as the others joined him. They hunkered in the bushes and silently watched the brakeman shunt the empty cars of the first train onto a siding. After uncoupling the engine it was shunted to a side track. There it slowly rolled down the incline hitting the first boxcar, slamming the cars together in a domino effect of crashing sounds until a new train was made up.

"Cars 'humpin'," Whiskas whispered.

The brakeman stepped between each car, checked the couplings, secured the air hoses for the brakes, and signaled to the engineer. The engine pulled away slowly at first, then gathered speed with the stack

---

* Gaycat = one inexperienced at riding the rails, or at hoboing.

belching black smoke and the wheels gripping the iron rails in a rhythmic clacking. Scottie stood fascinated by the power of this magnificent train. Even the dirt and grime falling on him from the clouds of smoke couldn't blank out the spell the fast moving train had over him. When the whistle sounded as the train cleared the yard, Scottie woke up to the fact that none of the hoboes had made an effort to board the train.

"Why didn't we catch that train?" he wondered out loud.

"Not goin' our way," Rod answered matter-of-factly. Perhaps Rod knew something Scottie didn't but he was wanting to get far away from this place as soon as possible. Each minute that passed found him getting more anxious.

The black man turned and stared at Scottie with dark eyes. A pale pink and gray soiled checkered bandana was wound around his forehead like a snake and tied at the side of his head with two ends dangling to his shoulders.

"Whad-yah say they's callin' yah?" the black muscular man asked, as he pulled out a small tin of tobacco from his shirt pocket. Pinching off a chaw with his fingers, he stuffed it between his discolored teeth and cheek. Brown drool slid from the corner of his mouth as he slowly chewed. He looked at Scottie with squinting eyes. "Your name is *Boy*, ain't that it?"

"No, my name is Scottie." He realized the word *boy* was a distasteful name to the black people and it offended him that this man should call him *boy*. "I'm Scottie," he boldly repeated.

"Musta misun'stood. You fixin' to go a bo-in?"

"Hoboin'?" Scottie stammered. "Of course that's what I'm aimin' to do."

"Bo-in' be a hard life *boy*."

Rod looked at the black man sternly. "No more, Checkas. Stop teasing Scottie. He's not a *boy,* he's a man like the rest of us. Hear?"

"Yes, suh, Rod," the man smirked as he bowed from the waist. Turning to Scottie again, Checkas retorted, "We's waitin' for t'otha train."

"Where's that train goin?" Scottie asked.

"South. Where it stops is where we're goin'." Checkas spat a glob of tobacco juice onto the ground, splattering Scottie's shoe. The hair on Scottie's neck raised and he felt his face flush like it did when he was about to lose control of his temper. Pulling up a bunch of grass, he quickly wiped the dark goo off his shoe. Although Checkas' sly smile infuriated him, Scottie determined to try to stay on the good side of this man that outweighed him by at least fifty pounds.

"Watch whatcha doin', Checkas," Rod commanded. The black man was still smirking when he turned his back on them.

"Conductah of that there freight is friendly," Rod explained. "He's been a-checkin' the yard. He knows where we's at. Added an extra boxcar for us. Yo-all have to notice these things." Scottie wondered how the conductor could see them huddled in the bushes, but reasoned the men's camp fire had tipped them off when the train first arrived.

"Extree car added maybe 'cause he likes hoboes. Maybe he has rel'tives that be bo-in', or maybe he just wants us to get the hell out of this town and on our way to someplace else," Whiskas added with a grin. Scottie tried to be inconspicuous as he stepped back away from the men for they stunk of sweat, smoke and cinders.

"Yeah, yo-all 'ill find a few brakemen sym-thetic to us'n up North," Checkas was saying, "but in the South, where's I come from, they's diff'rent."

"How's that?" Scottie asked politely.

"I've paid brakemen in the South money and they'd let me ride without botha," Whiskas answered. "Never approached the railroad bulls, though. They be mean. Two of my good buddies got kilt by those sons o' bitches. Shot them and left them dead like animals 'side the road just for hoppin' a ride. Damn bulls!"

The remaining train had been setting softly panting while waiting for the time of departure. Grasping the brake valve and ready to roll, the engineer faced the caboose and watched for the conductor's wave. It was a quick flutter toward the railroad police. The expectant hoboes knew it was their cue to run for the moving train, for now they knew where the "bulls" were. Slinging their bedrolls over their shoulders, they headed like marathon runners for the open door of the empty boxcar near the end of the train. The train rattled on the rails as the rods slowly pushed the pistons that turned the wheels. Smoke erupted from the stack and steam hissed from the brakes as the powerful train got underway. The white steam from the whistle filled the morning air in a scream of triumph.

47

"Keep them pants up!" Rod called to Whiskas. The old man's bedroll whacked against his back as he held tightly to the top of his pants, drawing the cuffs of the legs half-way up to his knees. Checkas and Rod led the way; threw their bedrolls into the car and then grasped the metal handle at the side of the open door. Using muscular arms to haul up their weight, they ran along beside the door, then lithely swung their bodies into the boxcar. Scottie followed their example but he soon found it wasn't as easy as he thought to catch a moving train. After two unsuccessful tries he let go of the handle and dove onto the hard wooden floor. Gasping for air he watched Checkas and Rod grab old Whiskas by his baggy clothes and hoist him onto the floorboards. Exhausted from the strenuous run, the men lay listening to the engine emitting a "chugh-a-chug, chugh-a-chug, chugh-a-chug" as it moved with added momentum out into the countryside.

Well worn wooden boards lined the entire inside of the boxcar. It was like riding in a drum with vibrations, sound of wheels turning on metal rails, and engine chugging all magnified inside the empty space. A series of shrill whistles --two long, one short, and another long--told the veteran hoboes that they were approaching a crossing. They were

They lithely swung their bodies into the boxcar.

48

safely away from the yards.

Scottie gazed through the door of the boxcar as the world flew by distancing him from his family. He hoped they missed him a lot, but doubted that anyone except his mother cared that he was gone. Convincing himself that the sooner he got his family out of his mind the better, he leaned back against the wall, concentrating on listening to the music of the wheels clacking and the wind whistling past the open door. The motion of the train soothed him. He felt relaxed and relieved that he was free from his father. Even his bruises didn't hurt as much. He had the feeling he was truly on a journey and he wondered what the men in the enclosure with him would do when the train finally stopped.

Rod and Whiskas sat with Scottie at the front of the boxcar while Checkas chose a spot alone in the middle of the car where he perched on his bedroll with hands folded and head lowered. Although he wasn't looking directly at them, Scottie had a strange feeling that he was being observed by the man with the half-closed eyelids. Checkas wore a double layer of singlets under a plaid jacket with missing buttons and ragged holes at the elbows. A large black toe protruded from one shoe like a turtle's head peeking out from its shell.

"Let's git that door shut fore'n I freeze!" Whiskas shouted above the clacking of the wheels. "They's a hi-ballin' for sure now!"

Scottie had his jacket buttoned up to his neck and was holding his bedroll tightly against his body for warmth while the cold wind whistled through the door.

"T'ain't col' in here a'tall," Checkas chuckled. "White folk just plain got thinny skin."

"Yo-all not bein' funny," Rod said approaching Checkas with clenched fists. The black man turned serious with dark eyes that studied the man standing over him. Scottie expected to see a fight right then and there and felt sure Rod would get the worst of it. Surprisingly, Checkas grabbed his bedroll and inched himself backwards to the far end of the car where he stayed for the rest of the trip, watching the men with sullen eyes.

Scottie felt uneasy at Rod's reaction. He couldn't see where Checkas had said anything bad enough to fight about. Rod, the soft spoken easy-going man, had shown a side that made Scottie wonder if he, too, had a hatred of blacks just like his father had demonstrated many times while donning his KKK outfit.

49

No one had tried to shut the door, so Scottie shakily worked his way across the swaying floor; visually checking the inside of the door for a handle. There was none, so he put his shoulder to the back of the door and pushed it along its track.

"Stop! Don't shut the door 'out no spike!" Whiskas roared. Scottie froze, holding the heavy door in position while he waited for Rod to reach outside the car. Yanking a spike from its bracket he quickly jammed the wedge* horizontally into the track.

"Thar!" Rod whooped, "that'll keep us from gettin' locked in this cage. Give 'er a shove now, Scottie!" The door stopped at the spike, leaving several inches open. When Scottie sat back down, he blinked constantly to keep the dirt and grain that was swirling around inside from getting into his eyes.

Checkas, sitting on his bedroll at the end of the car stared straight ahead--motionless. Other than pulling his jacket closed across his chest, he showed no sign of being cold or uncomfortable. He just blended into the wall against which he sat.

While Whiskas and Rod shouted above the noise around them, Scottie listened intently.

"Always been a professional bum," Whiskas said. "Ever since I could remember! Easier to ask for handouts than work!"

"Didn't yah evah have a wife or kids?"

"Nah! What I be wantin' a wife holdin' me back fer? I loves this life, and that's the plain truth of it!" Whiskas answered. "Yah got a wife?"

"Nah, just a special woman and some kin in the lone star state."

"Why'd yah take to the rails?"

"Lookin' for work. 'Sides, law was a-makin' my life a little miser'ble," Rod said, chuckling at his own thoughts.

* These wedges were stored in a U-shaped metal piece fastened outside each boxcar. They were used to secure the doors while the freight was in motion. Because of their shape they were often called "spikes."

Whiskas was a bum, clear and simple, and Rod had taken to the rails because he was in trouble with the police somehow. Scottie made up his mind he wasn't going to divulge anything about himself. These men had a previous life to tell about, or not to tell, just as they pleased. Right now it pleased Scottie not to tell them anything about himself.

The frightened boy of fifteen, who called himself Scottie, had joined the ranks of those riding the rails. Feeling a mixture of emotions ranging from freedom to confusion, he desperately hoped there was a better life at the end of the tracks.

The railroad men took pride in cleaning their monstrous engines

Photo taken at Essex, CT

Hobo Hospitality

Scottie shivered with excitement. His skin felt like it was too tight for his body and his head felt like it would burst with thinking about what lay ahead. Shifting his bruised body, he got as comfortable as he could by lying on his side with his head propped in his hands. This caused a problem for grain dust flew around his head. This along with the musty wood smell that got up his nose made him sneeze. Keeping his face tight to his jacket sleeve, he concentrated on what Whiskas and Rod were saying.

"Sure hope'n there's a decent jungle at the end of this line!" Whiskas's yelling could barely be heard above the clacking and rattling of the boxcar. "Couldn't get me any sleep last night. Bulls roamed the yards all night, makin' me nervous."

"Yeah, I hear yah!" Rod called back. "Thought we'd be caught for sure. Bad night, with a full moon to boot." Moving closer to Whiskas, he said, "Maybe you can catch a nap 'fore we reach next stop. We'll wake yah when your snorin' gets too loud!"

Whiskas stuffed his glasses into his coat pocket as he grinned at Rod. His wrinkly old face resembled a hairy grey prune.

"Guess I'll take yah up on that. I'll get a little shut-eye. But only 'til I hear whistle blow." Placing his hands on his stomach, he groaned, "God, my innards all botched up. I needs a good crap more'n I need sleep."

"Stick your ass out the door and go at it," Rod laughed.

Whiskas curled up in a ball without another word.

"Do yah usually sleep at night and ride the train days?" Scottie asked.

Whiskas raised his head and stared at Scottie in a way that made the boy know he had said something stupid.

"You ride at night less'n you want trouble. Can't be seen at night 'cause those railroad bulls ain't got no cat's eyes you know." Curling up again the man continued talking although his eyelids were closed. "If'n weren't for the man back there, we'd be stayin' in the bushes 'til evenin'. Night time we see lanterns swingin' and we can keep ourselves out of sight. You gets your sleep durin' the day in a jungle or 'side the road if'n you can't find a place that's hid from the tracks."

"We's sure to find a hobo jungle at the end of this line," Rod said putting his hand softly on the old man's shoulder. "Yo-all git sleep now Whiskas. Yah hear?" Whiskas pulled his enormous coat closer to his body, tugged his cap down over his eyes, and went to sleep looking as content as a hibernating bear.

Rod dragged Whiskas's bedroll over by his own and stared at Checkas with squinted eyelids. Scottie felt Rod's words of wisdom were meant for Checkas more than him when he said, "When yo-all ride the train you watch your belongin's and keep your eyes open for police. There's more safety in a jungle. *No one* there will steal from 'nother 'bo. Word gets 'round and his life ain't worth a damn. Don't evah steal from them what has less than yo-all."

"I'd never do that," Scottie replied. "There ain't nobody got less than me." Rod looked at him indicating he had heard, but changed the subject.

"Yo-all 'fraid of the bulls, Scottie?" The boy shifted his position again, dragged his nose across his sleeve, and waited a minute before answering. He didn't want Rod to know how hard his heart was thumping against his ribs. A cold chill started at the end of his spine and went clear to his head at the mere mention of the railroad bulls.

"Guess I'm 'fraid of being caught by the police. Ain't you 'fraid--ridin' in the day like this?"

"Phaw! No! This'n what you call an ex'eption. *The man* let us ride this here train. Would of had to start walkin' the tracks if'n he didn't take pity on us. There just warn't 'nuf cover there and we's all needin' sleep.

Even though Scottie had gotten little sleep the night before, he was too excited to think he could ever sleep again. Whiskas's head drooped to the side as he snored loudly. Rod looked at him, shook his head and laughed.

53

"Guess the ol' man'll have strength when he-all wakes," Rod said. "Whiskas was right in advisin' yo-all to ride the trains at night less'n you'd like a railroad bull whacking a night stick up side your head. They could do worse than that and no one would care. Saw a bull once make a man jump from the catwalk of a movin' train. No tellin' where poor devil landed. I would have gotten the same if'n I warn't ridin' the blinds of a passenger car where bulls couldn't see me. That sure was my lucky day!"

The rocking motion plus the steady rhythm of the rails were relaxing. Scottie sat beside Rod against the vibrating wall and watched the scenery flash by; a forest surrounded an open pasture, frightened cows ran in panic from the noisy engine and children stood in the yards waving at the train rumbling by. Scottie tightly held his bedroll and rode without thinking about where he was going. He was happy for the time being just to be away from his Pa.

After about two hours the throttle quieted down and the train slowed. When the whistle sharply announced the yard limits, Whiskas jumped up and grabbed his bedroll as if an alarm clock had sounded. All four companions lunged for the door. Rod was first to reach it and sliding it open, he quickly jumped out. A loud crunching of loose gravel sounded as his feet plunged to the ground. With gazelle quickness he slid down a slight embankment and disappeared into the cover of the brush. While the train was still moving, Whiskas and Scottie jumped simultaneously with their bedrolls slung over their shoulders. Checkas leaped off a few seconds later. Scottie stood watching, expecting the black man to join them, but without even a glance in their direction, he strode off to the other side of the tracks and disappeared behind some large maple trees.

"Come on," Rod called from the brush. "Don't be botherin' 'bout Checkas. He'll be junglin' up down the way." Scottie swung in behind Whiskas as Rod pushed through the thick undergrowth. Branches snapped back and slapped their bodies. The boy hardly noticed his painful bruises for he was concentrating on keeping up with these men.

When they finally came back out into open space, the train was more than a half mile away. Walking on the ends of the railroad ties and trudging in the loose gravel for another quarter of a mile brought them to a small sign. Written with pencil on a torn piece of cardboard were the words, 'WHITES ONLY."

"Didn't know hoboes were ag'in blacks," Scottie said.

"They's human, boy, they's human," Whiskas replied.

"Guess that's why Checkas headed other way?"

"It'd be my guess," Whiskas chuckled.

Scottie remembered how his father had punished him if he was even seen with a black person. Although he had no hatred for them, he wondered if the men riding the rails were like his father--full of hate and prejudice. Glancing back in the direction Checkas had gone he saw nothing but the trees that had engulfed him. Hurriedly falling back in behind Whiskas, he heard the welcome sound of a running stream as they approached a large clearing.

Scottie stared at this first hobo jungle he had ever seen. The grass and underbrush had been worn to hard-packed dirt by numerous feet. A crude fireplace made from a lop-sided circle of rocks was under the one big shade tree. A coffee pot with wisps of steam slipping from its spout sat on a make-shift grate over the fire. Large pieces of cardboard and sections of thousand-mile paper* littered the area. Several men sat around the fire while others slept on cardboards or on the ground. Those who were awake stared suspiciously at the new comers. When Whiskas waved and shouted, "Don't any of yah rec'nize old Whiskas?!" one of the older dissheveled men extended his neck to get a better look.

"Well, if it ain't old Whiskas! Thought you was buzzard bait long ago! Bring your friends in and have a cup of jo!" The man's grin revealed many missing teeth and he didn't seem to care that he was slobbering tobacco juice down his chin.

"Yeah, by gum!" sounded a booming voice, "need help getting together a gumbo." A short stocky middle-aged man hollered as he came from behind the trees. Red bushy hair hung to his shoulders and his full beard matched his sunburned, wind blown face.

"Sure would 'preciate somethin' in our bellies 'fore we catch the train out, Red," Whiskas announced. Since Scottie hadn't eaten anything since morning, gumbo sure sounded great. For the time being, a cup of strong black coffee kept his stomach from rumbling.

Rod sat on an upside down pail and slowly rolled a cigarette from

---

*Thousand-mile paper was a waterproof paper used around lumber yards and picked up by hoboes for insulation inside their clothes, to sleep on, or to protect them from the weather.

the pouch of tobacco he kept in his jacket pocket. Dragging slowly on the fag, he held his head back and watched puffs of smoke form rings in the clear air.

"I be Joe. Watcha call yourselves?" a grizzled old man asked with a distrustful look toward Rod and Scottie.

"Rod's my handle, and this be Scottie."

"You'll have to pardon my 'spicious nature today. We had trouble in the camp yest'day."

"You alright?! What happened? We'll even the score for yah!" Whiskas screamed as he jumped around at a lively clip like a boxer warming up for a fight.

"Bunch of Yeggs* came whilst we was out huntin' for fixin's for gumbo yest'day. Stripped the camp. Even took our banjo and bindles".**

"Why those sons o' bitches," Whiskas shook his head in disbelief and sympathy.

Joe slowly rose from the rock near the fire and hobbled to the bushes nearby where he retrieved a five-gallon can. After brushing it off with his coat sleeves, he tossed it toward Rod. It missed its mark and rolled along the ground, stopping next to Scottie.

"Take this to the stream and clean'er," Joe barked. "Get some water in it for the stew."

"Grab hold," Rod commanded Scottie. Each of them held a side of the can and headed for the stream where they scrubbed the inside with sand.

"How come the men does what the old guy tells them?" Scottie asked. "He seems weak 'nough so's he couldn't beat any one of them."

"He's king of this-here jungle," Rod explained. "Some men love the rails so much that when they's too old to ride anymore they don't want to go back home. He's like that. Considers hoboes his kin and keeps this camp open. The men respect him for that."

"Just 'spose someone comes along that doesn't want to do what he says?"

"Kings usually carry guns, too, so bettah do as he says. Notice that lean-to shack down by the edge of the clearin'?"

---

*Yeggs were hoboes turned thieves who were destructive and stole merchandise both on the trains and from the jungles. Their lawless acts gave a bad name to other hoboes traveling by freight.
**Banjo = frying pan; Bindles = bedrolls.

Rod sat on an upside down bucket at the hobo jungle

"Yeah, I noticed."

"That shack's the old man's only shelter."

"Looks like a Hooversville," Scottie murmured as he glanced again at the pitiful building.

"What's that?"

"Nothin'. Just somethin' I saw when I was a kid. Just thinkin' out loud."

"Oh," Rod shrugged his shoulders and nervously fingered his collection of safety pins. "Tough that Yeggs came in and stole from the old man."

"Are Yeggs some kind of foreigners?" Scottie laughed. "You 'fraid they'll steal your pins? The way you're holdin' onto them."

"No, I ain't afraid of them mean cusses. Sad part they makes their livin' by stealin' from their own kind at the hobo jungles. Once 'boes catch them, they's found dead. Nobody would tell police what happened to them even if they knew; police don't care anyway. Just more 'boes they don't have to chase. To them a dead 'bo is no bettah than a dead skunk squished in the road."

Rod took hold of the can. "Think this's 'bout as clean as we can get 'er," he said holding it up and watching the sun glint off its side. Clutching its rim, he started up the incline toward camp.

"Good job," Joe said running his finger around the inside of the can. "But, how's we gonna boil a stew without no watah?" Scottie's face flushed as Joe looked quizzically up at him. Rod just stood by and grinned. With the large can banging against his shins and laughter of the men in the background, Scottie ran back to the stream and laid the make-shift cooking pot on its side. Carrying it three quarters full of water was a struggle but he held it tightly and hefted it up the bank to the fire.

"Move that coffee pot. Make way for the boy," Whiskas demanded.

"While watah's boilin', you men find somethin' to put into this pot for stew. I'll stay here and guard your stuff." He patted his bulging pocket to assure the men he had a gun for his protection as well as to enforce his commands. With no idea which direction to take, Scottie followed the rest of the hoboes to town where they spread out and began asking for handouts.

The first farmhouse Rod and Scottie came to was fairly close to the road. Children could be heard inside, but everything became silent when Rod knocked on the door. No one answered his first knock, so he thumped loudly on the door and waited until a woman opened it a crack and called out, "Whatcha want?"

"We hate to trouble yo-all, M'am, but we was wonderin' if'n yo-all could give us a veg'table or two that we might cook for our suppah. My son and me ain't et in two days. We surely would appreciate a little kindness, M'am. We'd be happy to do some chores in exchange. Be glad to help you out, you havin' young'uns and all." As Rod bent over to peek through the narrow opening of the door, the woman's trembling hands held tightly to the edge of the door.

"Stay there. I'll be right back." She disappeared into the house and shut the door. They could hear her telling the children to stay out of sight. Rod winked at Scottie.

"Works ev'ry time. She's all nervous 'cause her man ain't home. Probably thinks we'd rape her or kill her or somethin'," he whispered. When the woman returned, she opened the door just enough to throw four carrots and two potatoes onto the step. They heard the bolt slide across the wood and slam into its locked position.

"Sure was a skittery one," Scottie said. "'Fraid of us. Could tell that."

"She had nothin' to worry 'bout. I wouldn't hurt her. Just playin' a game with her mind. Have to work on a person's symp'thy or fear, whatevah gets yo-all some food."

By the time they returned to the hobo jungle, most of the other men had already arrived with what they had scavenged. The carrots and potatoes were added to the pile on a newspaper beside the fire. Joe wiped the blade of his jackknife on his pant leg before cutting the vegetables and meat for the stew; then everything was thrown together into the can of boiling water. While waiting for it to cook, the men kept their minds occupied by playing cards, telling stories of towns they had been in, and laughing about how they outsmarted the railroad bulls.

Joe sat and tended the fire as flames licked the sides of the can, blackening it with soot. Every once in a while the ingredients were tested with a sharpened stick that served as a stirrer.

Whiskas had stayed at the camp when the others left for town. When they returned, he was laying on his back on a cardboard, snoring and moaning in his sleep. It was dusk and time to eat before Rod shook him awake. "Time to eat, ol' timer."

Those who didn't carry an eating bowl had long since found a can and washed it in the stream. Edward held the tin cup taken from home that morning. It made him homesick as he turned it around in his hands and felt its smooth sides. Memories of drinking from it only last night when his mother had saved his supper for him made him sad.

"Chow's on men!" Joe called while filling a metal spoon with the broth. After blowing on it, he popped it into his mouth. Hastily he spat it out! The response was so unexpected that the men silently looked at each other trying to figure out what was wrong with Joe.

"Damn!" he hollered as he scrubbed his lips with his hand. "What's goin' on here?"

"Burn your gullet did ye?" Red asked.

"Fussy old coot tonight ain't yah, Joe?" another said as he dipped his can into the stew.

"Taste it yourself you old Son of a Buzzard!" Joe shouted. "Then tell me what *you* think. You smart ass. Yah want this swill in your guts?"

As the rest gathered to get a share of the stew, Scottie filled his cup and sat cross-legged on the ground. Without the advantage of a spoon, he sipped a little of a most horrible tasting broth. Running to the stream, he took great gulps of cold water, swished it around in his mouth, then spit it back into the stream. What little liquid slid down his throat burned all the way to his stomach. The other men were running to the stream, coughing and gagging as they ran. Half-chewed food littered the ground.

"Tastes like gas to me," Red managed to blurt out in between his coughing and spitting. "Let's have a look at that can." Careful examination proved the can had been used for a gas container sometime in the past. The gas, activated by the heat, had spoiled their stew. With one mighty hard kick of his foot, Red sent the can and its contents sprawling over the ground.

While listening to the men swear and curse about their misfortune, Scottie scavenged a few pieces of vegetables, washed and rewashed them in the stream and ate them cold. He had to put something in his stomach, gas or no gas.

As the sun settled behind the trees, the men went to sleep -- some snoring, some tossing and turning, some so quiet you would think they were dead. Scottie's eyes stayed wide open for a long while staring up at the stars. Haunting thoughts came to his mind as he sorted out the conversations he had heard earlier of hoboes thrown off a train and even being crippled or killed by a railroad bull. For his mother's sake, he hoped he would not become another statistic in this world of hoboes.

He suddenly was startled by a noise in the bushes. He froze and was so silent he could hear his heart beating. Cautiously peering toward the sound, he half expected to see the Yeggs returning. Slumping down with relief, he watched four large raccoons amble into the camp, lap up the remaining stew, sniff at some of the men's bedrolls, and waddle back into the underbrush. Good luck to your stomachs, Scottie thought. Glad you like to eat garbage.

Through the quiet of the night, long, low train whistles blew. Each signaled they were coming into the yard limits. There was something soothing about those whistles. Scottie associated them with a new beginning for his life. He thought of running and hopping one of the freights, but considered it best to stick with the other 'boes for a day or two anyway. It was almost time for the sun to come up before he closed his eyes and went to sleep, exhausted from the excitement of his first day on the rails. Rod shook him awake at noon.

"Time to wake up and get into town for some chow. This time maybe we can get us somethin' already cooked," he said.

Scottie rolled himself to his feet, took a leak, and they were soon back on the road again.

A friendly farm lady gave them two bread and jelly sandwiches and a cup of milk apiece. Scottie was used to eating only one meal a day so this was a very pleasant start to his day. The sun seemed a little brighter and the world a little friendlier now that he had food in his stomach.

Arriving back at the jungle in late afternoon, they picked up their belongings and, along with five other men, headed out. This time they rode the top of the car, keeping alert for railroad bulls, and clutching the catwalk tightly as they rumbled over heavy ground.

Climbing the ladder to the catwalk

Hiking Through the Countryside

When riding the rails, you lose all track of time. Each day a new adventure for survival kept Scottie and Rod on the move from town to town and state to state. It was on a summer day that they happened to find a small jungle, hidden from the rail yard. A well-worn path took them to a clearing in the tall aspens. Approaching cautiously, they sat hidden with their backs against the giant trunk of an old fallen tree where they could study the few men sitting in a loose circle around a fire. They were passing a jug around. From the loud and noisy revelry, it was obvious to Scottie that they were drunk.

"They's drinkin' mighty early," Rod whispered. "Don't see any coffee pot or food."

"Guess that jug's their breakfast," Scottie replied.

"Yeah. They'll wish they had food in their stomachs 'fore long." Rod lazily stretched his arms upward. "'Specially if that's Pink Lady they's drinkin'."

"What's that? My Pa drank a lot, but I nevah heard of that."

"Pure alcohol made from sterno."

"Nah! You're kiddin' me! How could they do that? They drink that stuff?"

"Those that be desperate 'nuf squeeze it through their shirt, run it through a gumbo and cut it down. Never made it myself but hear it's pure grain alcohol when it's ready to be passed 'round." Rod stretched again, looking at the sky. "Sure's a great day." Scottie nodded as he watched the tiny puffy clouds floating across the azure blue sky.

"Where'd yah figure we're at?" Scottie asked.

"Some southern state. Didn't see no sign tellin' us where we's at."

"Think it's safe to sleep here today?"

"Naw. Bettah leave soon's we can. It's a perfect day for a hike," Rod answered. Weary from a night of dodging railroad bulls, Scottie didn't cotton to that idea at all.

"Think we could sleep over here away from the group? They'll soon be dead drunk anyway."

"Mostly him I don't trust." Rod cautiously motioned toward a tall dark man who strutted and danced around the group like a cock, challenging one man after another to a knife fight. "Old Feathers, there. Don't trust 'im." Brightly colored feathers fastened to the brim of a cowboy hat flew up and down as he gyrated among the men, flinging his knife into the ground near them. They guffawed at the man's antics and slapped each other on the back, rolling around crazily to miss the blade as Feathers pitched the knife at them.

"They ain't sober 'nuf to mind a mad man in camp, but I think we bettah get on down the road," Rod whispered. "Wouldn't feel safe sleepin' anywhere near that man. Don't make any sudden moves. Pick up your belongin's and follow me." Scottie reluctantly tucked his bedroll under his arm and trudged behind Rod back to the road as silently as they had come.

The narrow, tarred road cut a path through the countryside, separating the old houses and farmland like a narrow strip of black ribbon. Stone walls set the boundaries for milk cows and vegetable gardens. Dogs bounded from yards with friendly, or sometimes ferocious, warnings as Scottie and Rod encroached on their territory. Tall weeds held clusters of morning glories, and wild roses climbed the walls, wafting their perfumed bouquet through the clear air. Tiger lilies grew in abundance among the grasses with black-speckled orange-petaled heads nodding on long thin stems. Huge old maples and oaks spread their limbs over the roadway.

It was mid-morning when Rod decided to put the bum on an old farmhouse. It was a one-story wooden framed structure with wide, cracked and weathered shingles clinging to the sides like scales on a fish. Two massive wooden posts at each end held up the sagging roof of the veranda, which ran the full length of the house. The wide hand-hewn floorboards of the porch were warped and the ends had rotted away from dampness. One step up brought them onto the floor that groaned under their weight. The door, located in the center front, grated on neglected rusty hinges as a large man, shotgun in hand, faced them.

"What'cha want?" he growled.

"Please sir," Rod spoke quickly and quietly. "We mean no harm. Me and the boy just lookin' for a little work to do for a bite to eat." Scottie fidgeted for the man held his gun on Rod while he silently scrutinized them.

"Wants to work?" He pointed the gun at a pile of wood thrown in a heap like jack straws. "Split that wood over yondah and I'll give yah some grub."

"Be glad to, sir. And, thank you," Rod answered as he tipped his cap to the man and sauntered to the wood pile with Scottie following on his heels.

"I'll split. Yo-all stack," Rod said picking up the ax. Placing a chunk of wood end up on a large stump, he raised the ax over his head with both hands and swung down, splitting the wood in two with a loud snap. Scottie stacked as Rod cut until there was at least a cord of wood neatly stacked between two trees. Whacking the ax blade into the chopping block, Rod declared, "Let's go git our pay. Earned it today." Wiping their faces with their sweat-soaked shirt sleeves, they hurried onto the porch. Before they could knock, the man stepped out with two bowls of watery stew and a half loaf of homemade bread that had been around for a while.

"Eat outside," he grunted, putting the tray on the edge of the porch. "Leave the dishes when ye're through," he muttered as he disappeared into the house.

"This bread needs soaking in the stew," Scottie commented as he tunked it on the edge of the bowl.

"Not bad tasting, even if it is hard," Rod said after he swabbed the remaining gravy from his bowl with the last chunk of bread. "Let's get these bowls set beside the door and head on out."

"Got me a feelin' that man's standin' at the window with his shotgun ready just in case we try to steal his dishes," Scottie said, glancing back at the house.

"Yo-all could be right. Don't mattah though. We got what we wanted and he got his wood split and stacked. We's even."

At the edge of a cow pasture they made beds by bunching up the brown needles under a large pine tree. The scent of pine was over-powered by the smell of cow manure on the warm breezes blowing across the pasture. Smells didn't bother Scottie like they used to and he had no more trouble with his sinuses. Now sweaty body odors and musty clothes were a part of his life.

"Sure had some fun last night," Scottie said as he stretched out to rest.

"It was dang'rous hidin' in that boxcar. We could have got kilt," Rod reminded him.

"Goose bumps covered my body when I heard the railroad bull walkin' the catwalk and his club scrapin' 'gainst the car while he climbed the ladders. Knew he'd nevah find us."

"He sure traveled from car to car tryin' mighty hard to get a chance to whack our asses for us," Rod chuckled. "He saw us get into t'other car. Nevah did see us switch and hide 'hind that box. He was a-chasin' his tail all night." They rolled around the ground with laughter.

"He was thinkin' he'd either find us or kill hisself tryin'!" Scottie roared as he remembered how they had made a screen of Rod's black blanket and hid undetected behind a box in the dark corner. Maybe next time they wouldn't be so lucky with their game of hide-and-seek, he thought, but living on the edge of danger and outwitting the policeman gave him satisfaction enough for this day.

They soon were spent with laughter and Scottie contentedly closed his eyes and went to sleep.

When Rod reached out with the tip of his shoe and nudged him, Scottie leaped to his feet.

"Ow!" he moaned, whacking his head on a low overhanging limb.

"Glad yo-all's awake," Rod said with a smile. Scottie looked at the man sitting Indian fashion, hands folded between his knees. His unkempt hair hung to his shoulders and he looked scraggly with a week's growth of beard.

"You need a shave," Scottie noted. "Needs to get yahself cleaned up." Rod silently fingered his row of safety pins. The sun glinted off them like silver caterpillars clinging to the top of his overalls bib. Rod's sullen silence told Scottie it was best to drop the subject.

"You 'bout scared me to death nudging me like that. Thought the police had me for sure."

"Don't make no mistake. If those bulls had got yo-all, there'd be blood a-runnin' from a big split in your head, 'stead of the little smackin' yo-all gave yah-self."

"I guess," he replied, rubbing his head as Rod chuckled. Noting that the long shadows from the pine trees were spreading out into the pasture, Scottie asked, "What time do you figure it to be?"

"Late 'nuf to git us down the road. Maybe get some more grub. Suppah time now. Some farm lady 'round here might give us some leftovers."

They trudged the road, knocking on doors with no response. "Gotta be some one home somewhere," Rod said angrily. "They's prob'ly peekin' at us from behin' the curtains."

"Maybe men folk still in the fields and they's 'fraid. Think we could persuade them that we ain't gonna hurt them?" Scottie asked hopefully.

"Wouldn't believe us. Desp'rate hungry men lie, or worse, to get food."

"Guess we do look mighty dang'rous," Scottie said doubling over with laughter. "Specially you. Those pins bettah be hid. Looks like dang'rous weapons to me." They both plunked down and laughed uncontrollably at the absurd and frustrating situation they were in.

"Look at yo-self. Yo-all's no prize. Yo-all look like yah don't know what soap and wattah is." Scottie guessed Rod was getting even for the remark he had made earlier about Rod's need for a shave.

"You're right." Scottie agreed as he stopped laughing and bent over to adjust the cardboard used for a shoe sole. "Rocks on this road bruisin' my feet," he complained.

The purple sky overhead contrasted to the rosy red band of light from the sun setting along the horizon when Rod yelled, "We're in luck!" Throwing his cap into the air, he twirled around in a clumsy dance of joy.

"What's happenin' with yah?"

"Look!" He pointed to a sign cut into the bark of a large elm. "It's a cross!" (†)

"What's that to us?"

"It means food. People livin' here are religious. Some hobo cut this sign to give us a message. Yo-all just watch me put the riggin' on*. And ... try to act like yo-all got the fear of God in yah," he called over his shoulder as they rushed toward the house.

"Won't be no act. My Pa put the fear of God in me long ago," Scottie

---

* Put the rigging on = begged food from them.

67

replied bitterly.

Climbing over the rail fence, they passed Holsteins bunched together waiting outside the door of a freshly painted white barn. The house, on the other hand, was an unimpressive small one-story structure set back from the road. Its warped shingles were weathered gray.

"Guess there's no mistakin' where this man spends his money," Rod mused.

Scottie stumbled as he rounded the corner of the house and landed in a wild tangle of brush and weeds growing over an abandoned flower garden. One lone rose clung tightly to a thick shrub and clumps of small white flowers blossomed in the tall grasses below. Branches of wisteria grew up the side of the house with large clusters of purple flowers hanging limply over the door.

"Can tell this woman loves flowers," Rod commented. With his finger to his lips and ear to the door, he knocked softly. Creaking boards indicated movement inside. When the door opened a crack, an elderly woman peered out at them over the top of her glasses. She had large watery sparkling blue eyes.

Rod removed his cap and spoke in a soft voice. "No need to be a-feared of us, M'am. Me'n my boy here had it tough, but God always provides. We-all on our way up north. Been workin' bunchin' onions, balin' hay and pickin' fruit. Lookin' for honest work. Just felt God tellin' me to come to your door. We'll be glad to do chores for you in payment for just a crust of bread in the Lord's name, please." The woman stared at them with smiling sympathetic eyes. Scottie could tell the woman believed Rod's bull. As for himself, he didn't like deceiving her. When his guts ached for food, however, Rod could tell her whatever he wanted and he'd go along with it.

"I'm not one to turn any of God's children away hungry. Just wait here." As the unlatched door swung open, they could see the stout woman limp across the uneven kitchen floor. Strands of wispy white hair that had escaped from the bun knotted on top of her head hung down over her shoulders.

"Homemade bread," Scottie whispered as the yeasty warm aroma floated out the door.

"She's an angel straight from heaven," Rod replied in a hushed tone.

"Where yah headed?" Rod asked when Scottie stepped back a

few feet toward the weed patch that once had been a garden.

"You'll see," he said with a grin. Forcing his thin body through the tangle of brush, he carefully cut the stem of the red rose. By the time he disentangled himself from the thorny patch, the woman was handing Rod a lunch wrapped in newspaper.

"Here's sandwiches for you and the boy. May God speed you on your way back home. I'll be a'prayin' for your safety."

"M'am, I picked this rose for yah to take inside and enjoy," Scottie said as he shyly handed her the flower. "It's not right that it should be hid in those bushes." The woman's eyes brightened as she took the rose and tenderly cupped it in her hands.

"A beaut'ful flowah for a beaut'ful woman," Rod added. "And thank yo-all, M'am. God bless yo-all for your kindness!" Removing his cap, he waved to her as she stood in the doorway with the rose pressed to her cheek.

Jumping the rail fence surrounding the pasture, they sat on a large flat rock beside the road. Rod hurriedly peeled back the newspaper from a sandwich.

"Great day!" Rod exclaimed. "San'wiches with real buttah and thick slices of roast beef! It's our lucky day to have found this farm." He smiled as he handed Scottie the other sandwich.

"Was yah funnin' with that woman 'bout trustin' God?" Scottie asked after swallowing his first bite of sandwich.

"Whatcha mean?"

"Do you believe God is watchin' out for yah?"

"Sure. Watches out for us all the time."

"Oh," Scottie nodded. They sat in silence as they finished eating and then headed for the same stream the cows shared and got a cool drink of water.

"Why'd yah tell that lady I was your son?"

"Cause that's how you play on their symp'thy. Everyone feels sorry for a man with a fam'ly who works hard and is a'headin' home.

"I think she must have known you didn't live up North with that accent. Guess she just felt sorry for us. I always tried to be truthful, but seems like I live a lie and tell lies a lot since ridin' the rails."

"Think nothin' of it, Scottie. Yo-all do what has to be done to stay alive. If lies is what gets yah food for yah belly, then lies is what

69

saves your life. Nothin' wrong with that." Scottie felt Rod was right. They had to live by their wits to keep alive. They lived lies; told lies so often that it was hard to separate what was truth from what was imagination. Well, that's enough thinking about that, Scottie told himself. Had to get down the road. Didn't hurt anyone tellin' her that lie. Left her happy with her rose. That must count for somethin'.

They folded the newspaper and put it in their pockets for paper came in handy for many things when on the road; like insulation inside your clothes, lying on when the ground was damp, using for toilet paper, bunching up for a pillow, or for reading when you were bored.

"She was truly a kind woman," Rod stated.

"God bless yah!" Scottie yelled across the open pasture as they headed down the road looking for a railroad yard.

Lesson at the Crossroads

Whoooooo! Whoooooo! Whoo! Whoooooo! The sound of a heavy train traveling fast with thundering exhausts was approaching the roadway. The lonesome whistle sounding throughout the country-side gave Scottie goose bumps.

"Let's go. Track ahead. See if'n we-all catch that train at the crossin'!" Rod called, sprinting up the road with Scottie at his side. In an instant, there was comparative quiet as the throttles were closed.

"She's slowin' down." Rod said between gulps of air. "We'll catch 'er up yondah."

"S'pose cars all locked?"

"Cross that bridge when we come to it."

As usual, where the train was going didn't matter to either one of them. The lengthening of Scottie's stride caused the weight of his bedroll to smack his back each time his foot hit the ground. With the determination of a person running for his life, he pulled himself toward the train with arms pumping and his breath labored.

Scottie didn't notice when Rod veered to the right, cut across the grass, threw his bedroll into a boxcar, and with a leap swung himself inside. When Scottie realized he was alone and the slow moving boxcars were passing, he instinctively reached for a side ladder. His sweaty hands slid off the grimy rung. In desperation, he grasped the ladder at the back of the next boxcar and got a nasty jerk off the ground. He found himself swinging awkwardly in mid-air between two cars like a rag doll. When his legs doubled under him, he fiercely held to the ladder. Excruciating pain shot through his body as his knees whacked the macadam roadway, ripping his overalls and tearing skin from his knees. Hanging on with the tenacity and strength that fear gives, he was dragged along until he painstakingly managed

71

to get one foot up onto the ladder. Pulling his body higher, he shakily kept himself upright on the bottom rung.

Grabbing the ladder of a moving car is dangerous for you can
lose your life swinging into the gap between cars.

Climbing with torn and bleeding knees was slow and torturous. His wounds throbbed and several times he thought he would pass out. Biting his lip to keep from screaming, he crawled off the ladder and onto the top of the boxcar. Exhausted, he clung to the catwalk with both hands. The train rumbled on, spouting smoke, and highballing through the evening air. Cinders from the stack landed on him and smoke choked his breath off, but that was the least of his worries. Staying on top of that swaying train was all that mattered. There was only time to think of steadying himself and reaching the next freight yard alive.

It seemed like hours before the train slowed for the next rail yard. Scottie spotted Rod with a group of men who jumped from the train and scattered toward the safety of the bushes.

"Rod, I needs help!" he screeched.

"By God, Scottie, is'n that yo-all up there?" Rod called looking up as he ran beside the train into the yard. "Yo-all got to get off 'fore the bulls start huntin' for strays."

"My knees all tore up," Scottie said. "Can't hardly move."

"Got to get off'n there!" Rod commanded. "Hurry! Get to the laddah and git down. I'll catch yah if'n yo-all fall."

Scottie knew Rod was right. He had to get off the top of the boxcar unless he wanted a beating by the railroad bulls. Dragging his stiff aching body backwards along the car, he forced his legs to go down the ladder until his feet were within jumping distance of the ground. Rod grasped his arm and yanked him out from between the cars. Putting his arm around the boy's waist, he half-carried, half-dragged him into the brush at the outer limits of the yard to the safety of a hobo jungle.

"Anyone got any medicine?" Rod asked as Scottie collapsed to the ground. "The boy's been hurt."

Scottie groggily looked at the blurred images of men standing around him, cringing as someone touched his knee with water and then flicked out particles of gravel that were embedded there.

"Anyone got a bottle on his hip?" Rod asked of the men.

"Sure. Don't use more'n you need though," another cautioned, handing Rod a bottle of muscatel.

"Hang on Scottie," Rod said. "Gonna sting a bit."

Scottie gasped as alcohol was poured into his open wounds.

73

Embarrassed by his show of weakness in front of this group of men, he was relieved when his knees were finally bandaged up with strips of cloth and he was no longer the center of attention. He fell back, exhausted, and went to sleep.

Rod stayed with him at the hobo jungle for several days until he was healed enough to head for the rails again.

****

"Next time we go catch a train, I get on first and you ride the top," Scottie jokingly told Rod. Limping along beside the man as they started for the road again, he grinned as Rod playfully punched him in the arm.

"I'm gettin' old, Scottie, but I can still outrun yo-all. Watch me catch the next train out. Yo-all 'ill be hangin' onto the caboose with the wind carryin' your skinny body straight out like a pokah. That would be a sight worth seein'!"

"I 'suppose that's why yah waited with me while I got my legs back. Just wanted to see me do that fool thing ag'in." Although Scottie laughed at himself, he made up his mind he'd stay behind before he'd ever try to climb the ladder between two cars again. There were just some lessons worth learning the first time around.

Louisiana Flatland

The sun beat down on the two weary travelers trudging across the Louisiana Flatland. Heat waves blurred the horizon and the tires of the few cars that passed churned up clouds of dust that stuck to the sweaty hitchhikers.

"Wish we'd find a rail yard," Scottie moaned. "I'm roasted."

"We'd be on a train if'n those damn police hadn't caught us on the outskirts of their town," Rod answered.

"Sure 'nuf didn't care for us. It was rather neighborly of them though to take us in their police car, makin' sure we'd get t'other side of their town line," Scottie replied sarcastically.

"It happens," Rod answered indifferently. "Better they kick us outta their town than put us in their jail or on their chain gang."

"That's for sure."

Walking in silence, they watched the heat waves in the distance, hoping for a breeze or a shade tree to give them some relief.

"Must be 200 degrees," Rod lamented as he adjusted his bedroll. "This rope's rubbin' my shoulder raw." Swiping his arm across his sweat drenched faced, he removed his cap and fanned the hot air around his head.

"Damn! I'm hot!"

"Trees ahead!" Scottie shouted with all the enthusiasm and relief of the lookout on a ship sighting land.

"Naw. A mirage," Rod scoffed. "Brain's fried so's yo'all seein' things." In spite of his doubts he increased his stride in order to keep up with Scottie. Nearing what had been dark silhouettes hugging the horizon a short while ago, they noticed leafy branches, limbs and trees taking shape. Shade from knobby twisted boughs welcomed the vagabonds.

"An abandoned orchard!" Rod hooted as they raced toward this oasis. "Maybe there's fruit!" Leaving their tattered shoes and bedrolls by the road, they joyfully ran barefoot through the dried brown grass.

"Worms nevah botha me. Makes the peach sweetah," Rod laughed picking up a fuzzy pink fruit full of worm holes and popping it into his mouth. While he hoggishly chewed the fruit and spit out the pits, Scottie crawled on the ground looking for droppings. Each leathery small shriveled peach, along with those half-rotten, were ravenously devoured.

"Man, I'm tired," Scottie moaned spitting out the last pit and rolling onto his back.

"We'll take a nap 'fore we-all push on," Rod declared as he stomped down the tall grass to make himself a bed. Exhausted from the heat, they were soon asleep.

Scottie woke up abruptly as a snake slithered across his outstretched arm. Jumping to his feet, he shook it off and stood trembling as its long thick black body quickly wriggled off into the grass.

"That was some big un," Rod grinned. "Glad it didn't bite yah."

"Just startled me, that's all," Scottie replied, trying to make light of his action although his heart was pounding rapidly. He was well aware of poisonous snakes in the area. Rubbing his arm to get rid of the feeling of the snake's cold moist scales, he said, "Better get goin'. Gotta try to find a train." Hastily pulling on his dusty shoes, he picked up his bedding, and headed for the open road where he and Rod walked another three miles before reaching a rail yard.

"Might know. No shade," Scottie said disappointed. "Only more flatland. Railroad station and that pile of coal ain't no help." Two men, black from coal dust, stood up and watched suspiciously as Scottie and Rod came nearer.

"I'm Rod and this here's Scottie. Don't mind if'n we wait with yo-all for a freight do yah?"

"Suit yourself. We don't own the yard." The rather stocky man whose leathery skin had tanned nutbrown plunked back down at the edge of the coal pile. "I'm Brownie."

"Just call me Denver Dan," replied the younger man.

"Yo-all been waitin long?" Rod asked.

"Since noon," Brownie answered. "May be stuck out here in the middle of nowhere. No trains are stoppin'."

"Gotta be action 'round here. No grass growin' 'tween the tracks," Rod observed. "That's a good sign. 'Sides, there must be a man in station ovah there. Leastwise door is open and windows ain't boarded. This gotta be an active rail."

While the men made small talk, Scottie watched them from his seat on a railroad tie.

"I could use some coffee. Anyone got fixin's?" Denver Dan asked. No one answered. Following a few minutes of silence, he continued, "You got water?" He looked hopefully toward Scottie's bedroll.

"I ain't got water," Scottie answered. "Guess can't make coffee."

"Here's coffee if'n someone comes up with watah," Rod said pulling a tin from his bedroll. Scottie recognized it as the tin that had been in the farmhouse where they had eaten the day before. How Rod stole that coffee was a mystery that was better left unsolved and unmentioned.

"Guess it's up to me," Denver Dan said reluctantly taking a water jar from his gear. Pulling the brim of his cap down over his eyes, he squatted and stabbed his pocket knife into the hard dry ground, picking at the dirt until there was a hole large enough for a fire. "That oughta be deep 'nuf," he said. "Put dry sticks or somethin' in 'er and get 'er goin'." The men picked up litter strewn over the ground and threw it into the hole. After starting the fire, Denver plunked himself down at the edge of the coal pile. Looking slyly at Brownie he said, "I did my share. If anyone got a pot bettah bring it out."

"All right, seein' we got water and coffee, I'll be sharin' my pot with yah," Brownie grumbled as he knelt over his bedroll and pulled out a coffee pot. The fire had taken hold immediately and pieces of coal kept it going. True to his word, Denver poured the precious tepid water into the pot. This was a sacrifice on his part, for all hoboes carried water with them whenever they could, just in case they got stuck in a boxcar for hours.

"Wish a train would hurry up," Rod grumbled as they drank the black coffee. Holding a can by the rim, he slurped from it, anxiously keeping an eye on the tracks. "We gotta get outta this hell-hole."

"We've been here a long while and ain't seen but one train, and it went hiballin' past," Brownie added. Then he smiled as though reassuring himself. "One'll be stoppin', sooner or latah."

"Never seen so much heat, even for Louisian'," Denver Dan ventured. Except for an occasional slurping noise, the men fell silent while tensely listening for any humming of the tracks. A grin crossed Denver Dan's face when he put his ear on the rail for the tenth time.

"Rail's rumblin'! Train's comin'!" he called. They scurried to the back side of the coal pile like a flock of chickens chased by a barking dog. The sound of steam from the brakes was heard before Denver Dan crawled over to the edge of the coal pile to get a look at the train. "A freight," he whispered. "Can't tell if any bulls are roamin' the line."

"Don't see a one," Rod said while eyeballing the length of the train. "Sun's too hot for 'em. If there are any police, they's prob'ly in the buildin' jawin'. Guess it's safe to finish the coffee."

Horses came alongside the train pulling heavily loaded creaking wooden wagons. As the first wagon stopped at a reefer, workers started unloading boxes of apples. Brownie took this opportunity to win the confidence of the drivers by boldly walking over to them. Running his hands down the glistening sweaty chestnut-colored sides of the horses

Scottie watched the men from his seat on a railroad tie.

he laid it on pretty thick about what wonderful horses they had. Soon they were jabbering away like old friends.

"Men gave me the word," Brownie said as he sauntered back to the coal pile. "They's leavin' in 'bout an hour. One empty reefer. Rest all gonna be packed and secured."

"Crawlin' into a 'frigerata car sounds good 'bout now," Rod sighed. He kicked a little coal dust onto the fire.

"They got ice in them cars?" Scottie asked, for it didn't seem possible ice could survive in this hot place.

"Sure," Rod answered. "Gotta have ice to keep stuff cool, so's it won't rot."

"Didn't see 'em load ice," Scottie said.

"They's already loaded. Gets it up north. Cuts it off'n frozen ponds and keeps it in the ice houses with hay for insulation 'til it's needed," Brownie explained. "Packed in Pennsylvania or some place like that."

"We can't crawl into no box with ice. That's worse than this heat. We'd freeze to death."

"Won't be crawlin' in with no ice," Brownie chuckled. "They pack them boxes plumb full of ice and keeps the doors locked when loaded. Reefer we head for is the empty one that ain't got no ice."

"Hearin' yah talk 'bout reefers reminds me of a story." Denver Dan began. He shook his head as though he was gathering his thoughts. "Man I knew tried ridin' reefer. T'warn't ice in it but the door was missin' its iron bar. He was a stubborn fool. Wouldn't listen." Denver looked sad and serious as he gulped a few times before continuing. "So anxious to git home, he propped door open with a stick and took his chances. Last I saw him he was disappearin' down the laddah into the box. Hear'd tell a man was found dead in a reefer in Georgia. Stick jiggled loose and door slammed down, shuttin' him in. Felt sorry for the poor fellah for I always had a gut feelin' t'was that same man who had been a friend to me. He was just tryin' to get home. Guy shoulda just waited. Shoulda listened."

Scottie sat on the railroad tie holding his head in his hands. Without a hat, it seemed as though the sun's rays penetrated clear through his skull and into his brain. He figured if he drank some coffee the queasiness in his stomach would go away. With weak and shaky legs he staggered over to the coffee pot and stood for a minute examining the reefers and boxcars that made up the long freight train. The huge monster blew off vapory clouds of steam. The roof door on one reefer was held open with a metal rod just as the workers had told Brownie it would be. Scottie felt like he would burst with happiness. He was becoming addicted to riding the rails and his whole body quivered as he thought of the thrill of traveling again.

He had just taken a gulp of coffee when Denver Dan let out a roar. "I'll be! It's a mirage I'm a-seein'! I'll be damned if'n it ain't Mama Sal!"

Scottie stared at a large woman boldly marching toward them from around the coal heap. Her parched lips widened into a grin that spread across her dark tanned face. Resting on her out-of-control thin wavy gray hair was an old straw hat with a wide brim that flapped like bird's wings in flight. The man's plaid shirt she wore with buttons missing hung loosely from her shoulders. Large breasts strained against the tight sweater under the shirt. Scottie took his coffee and sat down, but found it hard not to gawk at this mountainous woman and the short man wearing a camel-hair winter coat that hung almost to his shoetops. He nervously pushed his glasses back up to the bridge of his nose while a shy grin showed four rotted front teeth.

"Too bad you got your old man with yah, Sal!" Denver Dan winked at her. "You'n me could've had ourselves a good time." Sal's tanned skin took on a tint of red.

"Wouldn't be havin' the likes of you!" she roared. "I've seen you in

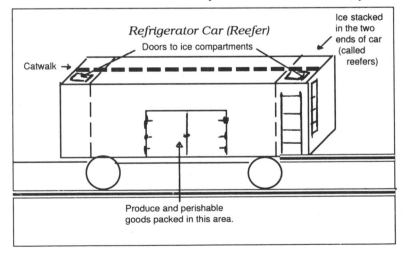

Refrigerator Car (Reefer)

action!" Laughter turned her face crimson and set her off coughing so hard that she almost choked. Amused by the odd couple, Scottie sipped his coffee, keeping an eye on their every move. He was intrigued with the meek little man and this boisterous woman who had brought a refreshing diversion to the discouraged group of men.

"You're plumb outta luck, Dan. Got me all I need right here," Sal proclaimed, roughly grabbing the small man and hugging him so

Mama Sal brought a refreshing diversion to the discouraged group of men.

tightly that her body engulfed him like a large feather pillow. The men hooted and hollered. As soon as he was released, he stepped backwards and nervously dragged the tip of his shoe back and forth in the dust.

"Elmer, come meet Denver Dan!" Mama Sal called.

"Yes, Love," Elmer mumbled. He nodded toward Dan, but kept a distance between him and the group.

"Welcome to some java, if'n some left," Brownie motioned toward the coffee pot.

"Fetch a cup of coffee, Love!" Sal bellowed as she plunked down near the coal pile. Her pants were held up with a braided belt and the pant legs were rolled up just below her knees. While she massaged the calves of her muscular legs, Elmer rummaged through his bedroll.

"Don't be movin' so fast, Elma," Brownie laughed, "You'll be givin' yourself a stroke." The suggestion was ignored as the man grabbed a tin cup, wiped its rim on the inside lining of his coat and hurried toward the coffee pot. After handing the coffee to Mama Sal, he slowly began what looked like a sacred religious ritual. Removing his coat, he folded it neatly and placed it on the ground. A small brush from his shirt pocket was used to meticulously whisk the coal dust aside until a two-foot wide spot on the ground was smooth with hard packed dirt. Crossing his ankles and bending his knees outward, he gracefully slid to the ground where he sat cross-legged beside his coat. As he stared through his dark rimmed glasses, Scottie couldn't help but feel sorry for the man who reminded him of a frightened caged owl.

"Dang good coffee. Sure on the hefty side," Sal said between noisy slurps.

"Special blend. Liked by farmas real well," Rod said as he glanced knowingly at Scottie.

"Travel with Elma all time now Sal?" Denver Dan asked.

"Sure do!" Laughter rocked her six-foot frame as she slapped her thigh with a loud crack. "Elma needs some-un to protect him from folks like you on the rails. Ain't that right, Love?"

"Yes, Dear," Elmer murmured as he shoved his glasses onto the bridge of his nose.

"How's come you two landed in this hellish town?" Brownie asked.

"Been pickin' apples," Sal retorted.

"No! Not you and Elma?!" Denver Dan slapped his hand to the side of his face and stared in disbelief. "In all this heat?"

82

"Yup, heat 'n all. 'Bout broke my back. Thought we'd work long's we could. That old boss-man worked us like animals! I just up and told boss-man we was sick of him and we was quittin'. Shoulda seen his face when's I told him what he could do with his job!" After an outburst of guffawing, the men grew silent and Scottie retreated into his own thoughts. He remembered the boss-man he and his Pa had worked for picking cotton when he was a kid. He could sympathize with how they felt; having to stay in the hot sun, knowing someone was watching you, and realizing the pay at the end of the day would be small reward for what you had endured.

Elmer slowly dragged an apple from his coat pocket and slyly passed it to Mama Sal. This did not go unnoticed by the others, but no one would consider asking for one themselves.

"We hafta share with all the men," Sal said as she vigorously polished the apple on her shirt sleeve. "Damned if'n they ain't shared their coffee with us. We need to be a'givin' them somethin' for their bellies. 'Sides di'nt cost us nothin'." Her body rocked with merriment. "Stole them. What's a farmah need with trees full of apples?" Elmer tossed an apple to each hobo, grinning like a child handing out presents on Christmas day.

The crisp MacIntosh cracked loudly when Scottie bit off a chunk and let the sugary juice run down his throat. Munching slowly, he was thankful for the sweetness that took the acrid taste of black coffee from his mouth.

"You headin' west?" Sal asked Brownie.

"Yup. Followin' crops. I'm one of those fools who works like a slave so's I won't be called a bum. I got some pride left."

"Out west they'll call yah a bum whether's you work or don't. Leastwise that's the smart mouth I got from the boss when we were pickin' out west." Sal frowned and stared straight ahead for a couple of minutes. "Oh, hell, who cares what they call us? We know who we are and what we're doin'. That's good 'nuf for me." As she spat these words out, Sal agilely jumped to her feet. She was like no woman Scottie had seen on the rails before. Most of the girls cut their hair short and tried to pass for men, or had a daddy with them to whop any man that got near them. Pity the man that tries to whop her, Scottie thought. She'd probably take on the best of them--and win.

"See yah been collectin' pins," Sal said staring at Rod who was carefully organizing them according to size and fastening them onto his overalls.

"Sure do." Rod proudly held out one of his political pins. "Collects these too. Surpisin' what yah can find layin' on the ground."

"Could you spare a couple of safety pins for my shirt?" Sal asked, holding the two sides of her shirt widely open. "If you don't mind giving up a couple that is."

"Sure 'nuf. Yo-all can have what yo-all want," Rod said as he chucked a few large safety pins in her direction. "Always like to help a fella trav'ler, 'specially a lady."

"There, look like a respect'ble woman now," Sal said, twirling around like a fashion model to show her pinned shirt. "Sides now the wind won't be freezin' any of my 'portant parts." Elmer blushed and squirmed uneasily at Sal's frankness while the men howled with laughter.

Bantering back and forth with words, each avoided and carefully concealed anything personal about his background for men on the rails were uncomfortable and mistrusted those that took too much of an interest in them.

The sun balanced on the edge of the horizon, turning the sky into a streaked pink and red tapestry. The evening breeze brought some relief as the group kept the train under surveillance. Sitting with their belongings beside them, they watched the brakemen slide the doors of the metal cars shut. After they locked them securely, they double-checked each door as if they didn't trust themselves to do it right the first time.

Scottie kept his eyes on the loosely closed top door of the empty reefer.

"Train headin' west 'bout seven," Brownie reminded them. "Headed to Californee. Bettah get ready."

"We'll be a-takin' it," Sal stated emphatically.

RIDIN' IN THE REEFER

Steam screeched from the boiler and the stack puffed black smoke. The train was ready to roll. Scrambling over the loose coal at the edge of the pile, Scottie swiftly bounded toward the empty refrigerator car. With the train slowly moving out of the yard, the group of vagabonds shoved and dragged each other up the ladders and onto the top.

"Get off the car you bastards NOW!" A lone railroad bull had appeared from seemingly nowhere and resolutely chased the train.

"Come 'n git us down why don't yah?!" Denver Dan yelled. Scottie stepped backward toward the ladder when the policeman deftly climbed up onto the roof of a car, ran its length, and vaulted from car to car. Straining his eyes, Scottie watched for any sign of a gun in the man's hand.

"Stand 'n face him!" Rod commanded. "He can't throw all of us off!" Scottie knew he had no choice but to stand with the rest. Even dying seemed better than leaping from a moving train and staying another few hours, or days, in the sweltering Louisiana flatland.

The train slowly picked up speed. They were leaving the gravelly yard behind when the bull reached the car closest to the hoboes. He stood and glared indecisively for a few seconds before shouting, "Don't ever let me catch any of you on my line again!" Then climbing part way down the ladder of the boxcar, he leaped and rolled onto the dried brown grass like a trained athlete.

"Glad he 'cided what's best for 'im," Rod said smugly as he grasped the metal rail circling the reefer door and swung it open. He quickly descended the ladder into the darkness below with Scottie, Denver Dan and Brownie following. Although it was tight quarters for four people, their body heat didn't stop Scottie from shivering.

"Cool in here," he said through chattering teeth. Screwing up his

85

eyes he looked up at the graying sky overhead.

"Lot warma than t'would be if'n there were ice in here," Rod laughed.

"You're right. I should be grateful for a little coolness."

"We safe in here?" Denver Dan's voice quivered. Scottie could smell the man's frightened sweat. "Yah sure the door won't slam shut?" Denver said starting back up the ladder.

"The door's propped open," Brownie said. "Can't yah see some light shinin' in here? Gettin' a mite skittery, ain't yah?"

"I suppose," Denver replied meekly as he climbed back down the ladder. Scottie was thinking about the man Dan had told them about who had died in a reefer and imagined Denver had the same thing on his mind.

"Wondah where Mama Sal and Elma be at?" Rod asked.

Rod grasped the metal rail and quickly descended the ladder into the darkness of the reefer.

"Since this reefer is empty, more than likely the reefer on other end was unlocked, too," Brownie said.

The men huddled together listening to the rumbling of the train on the tracks. Placing their bedrolls at their backs, they kept their bodies away from the cold damp walls. When they felt safe, they crawled up onto the top of the refrigerator car and waved at Mama Sal and Elmer who were seated in the middle of the catwalk.

Rod stood up, turned his back and peed over the side of the car. "Nothin' like pissin' into the wind," he said. "Makes yo-all hooked on ridin' the rails." The rest of the men stood on the swaying car, making a contest of who could pee the longest stream. They laughed heartily at Elmer when he held his coat tail up with one hand in an effort to stop the wind from splashing urine onto his large coat.

Bouncing along on top of the car, Scottie's skin tingled as the cool, dry air rushed across the train. His mind wandered to home and family, but he still had no desire to go home. Hatred of his father that had started him traveling was no longer the incentive for riding the rails. It was a strong feeling he had for the motion of the trains. Riding on top of the old rattler, he watched the changing panorama. Dark shadows contrasted with the moon shining on the fields and light flashing from windows of houses. He felt a closeness and kinship to the hoboes like they were a big family with jungles and boxcars for homes.

These happy thoughts continued until an image of his father's face forced itself into his mind. He nervously looked around for something to do to clear his thoughts. Standing while the train was highballing was a dangerous thing to do, but he felt he had to do something, though, to get his mind off his Pa.

"Gonna walk the catwalk and back!" he shouted to Rod.

"Don't be a fool!" Rod yelled as he tried to grab him. Avoiding the man's hand and filled with the confidence of a 15 year old boy, he started out. Mama Sal's arms flailed in exaggerated gestures as she shouted for him to go back, but he swaggered along being driven by the wind at his back like a drunken sailor on a rolling deck. Sal and Elmer crawled ahead of him toward the safety of their reefer.

"Stay!" Sal screeched. "Stay with us!" Scottie waved her aside and confidently turned to go back to the front of the car. Wind, smoke and red hot cinders now buffeted his body. Straddling the catwalk, with head lowered into the wind, it took all of his strength to finish the length of the car. Twice his feet slid causing him to fight to keep his balance so he wouldn't tumbler over the edge. His heart pounded against his ribs and his legs were like jelly when he sat back down.

"Stupid!" Rod yelled at him. "Coulda gott'n kilt!"

"Naw, not me," Scottie replied with a tremble in his voice. He had done a foolish thing, but his mind was now freed of thoughts of his Pa.

"Might be fun!" Denver Dan called. "Boy can do it, so's can I!"

"Don't be a fool!" Brownie's words disappeared into the black smoke swirling around them. Denver Dan was halfway down the length of the car when one long whistle blew. Whoooooo!

"Tunnel!" Brownie bellowed. Like scared rabbits, Scottie, Rod and Brownie disappeared into the safety of the reefer. Seconds later they were engulfed with the total darkness of a tunnel. Scottie tore off his shirt and tied it around his mouth and nose to keep the smoke and cinders that were gathering in the box from filling his lungs. Even then, what filtered through the cloth made him dizzy and sick to his stomach. He brushed away the red hot cinders that landed on his bare arms and back. Keeping his eyes tightly closed kept cinders from sticking to his eyeballs. He was beginning to think there was no end to the tunnel when Brownie exclaimed, "We're through the tunnel! Can see stars overhead!"

"Let's get topside," Rod said with relief as he grabbed the ladder. Scottie quickly put his shirt on and followed the men to the roof. Mama Sal had her head stuck out of the reefer at the other end of the car and waved at them with a big grin as she hoisted herself onto the roof. Elmer was close behind her.

"Where's Denver?!" Rod shouted, gesturing wildly. Mama Sal shrugged and pointed to them.

"I think he fell off the train!" Brownie hollered.

"S'pose he could've got knocked off with the knotted ropes?"

"Those ropes ain't heavy 'nuf to knock a man down. Maybe got s'prised and fell off," Brownie added. They all lay flat on their stomachs peering over the side, hoping to see Denver Dan dangling from the train. Disappointed, they crawled back toward the catwalk.

"He should've heard the whistle," Rod said sadly.

"Same signal wails for a tunnel as for a crossin'."

"Oh, no," Mama Sal said as she wiped her eyes with the corner of her sooty handkerchief. "Sure hope he didn't fall on the tracks."

"Do you think he's dead?" Scottie asked, saddened at the thought.

"Best he be dead than broke up inside that tunnel," Brownie moaned. They sat glumly listening to the clack-clack-clack of the wheels speedily carrying them away from any help they might have been able to give Denver Dan.

Scottie drew his knees up under his chin and wrapped his arms around his legs. He felt guilty. It was him that should be missing now instead of Denver Dan. He should never have done such a fool thing as to walk the length of the car. If he'd fallen, his mother would never have known what had happened to him. A longing for his family was getting ahold of him. Right about now he wouldn't even mind seeing that sonofabitch he had for a father.

The sorrowing group huddled together until the whistle signaled the approach of a rail yard. That lonesome whistle set them into action. It signalled the end of their mourning. Quickly retrieving their gear from the reefers, they were off the train and scrambling through the loose rolling gravel before the brakes had brought the train to a stop. They ran into the gray morning, away from the lights of the station.

"Got to get these damn cinders outta my eyes," Brownie said, holding his eyelids wide open to keep his eyeballs from getting scratched.

"Ridin' through that tunnel was sure hell," Rod agreed.

"Sun looks like a big silver ball this mornin'," Sal said. "Heat haze gives it a peculiar look, but guess it's shinin' good 'nuf so's I can get the cinders out of your eyes. Anyone got a wooden match?"

Rod fumbled in his pockets and came up with a match. Scottie watched while Sal sharpened it with a jackknife. Amazingly her steady hands held the match and flicked the cinders out of the men's eyes and off their eyeballs without hurting a one of them.

"How come yo-all got no cinders, Sal?" Rod asked.

"Elmer and me, we just put his coat over our heads. Got a few holes in it from hot cinders rainin' on us; that's all."

After clearing the men's eyes, Sal turned to Elmer. "Come, Love, let's head for town. Buy some liquor and forget our troubles for a while." Without a word, he fell in behind her and with a wave of the hand, they disappeared down the narrow tarred road.

Rod, Scottie and Brownie lost no time in discovering a small camp.

Then they headed for town to put the rigging on some generous soul for their breakfast. Because begging didn't work out, they decided to break in and steal something to eat. The first promising thing that Brownie noticed was a henhouse setting a little ways from a barn.

"You're the skinniest, so you go for some eggs or a hen while we watch out. We'll whistle if anyone comes so you can hightail it out of there."

As soon as Scottie slid through the narrow door and tried to grab a chicken, they flew against the walls in panic. Feathers drifted through the air as they squawked in fright. Slipping and sliding on chicken manure, Scottie hastily took the eggs from under the setting hens while they angrily pecked at his hands. When he had what eggs he could find safely in his pockets, he escaped out the door, leaving it swinging.

"Good job," Brownie said as they raced through the hay field. "How many eggs did yah get?"

"Didn't stop to count. We got enough. Long's I get back to camp without them breakin'."

"Evah eat one raw?" Rod asked.

"Sure," Brownie said, "but ain't a'feelin' like it now."

"Let me have one," Rod said holding out his hand. While jogging down the road, Rod cracked the egg with his fingers, tipped his head back and let the insides slide down his throat. "Gives yah en'gy!" he whooped as he put on an extra burst of speed.

****

Back at the hobo camp, a fire was blazing away. Rod heated a flat piece of metal and scrambled the eggs on it, stirring them with a stick until they were cooked. Scottie had never eaten eggs that tasted any better than that breakfast. After eating, he lay down on the hard ground to sleep, but his thoughts wandered to home and family. What if he had fallen from the train instead of Denver Dan? Would anyone really care? Naw, he decided, nobody'd care what happened to him. Depressed, he fell into a fitful sleep. A vivid nightmare of Denver Dan with a crowd of railroad bulls throwing him over the side of the train frightened him. When he woke up in a sweat, it was late in the day and Rod was the only man left in camp. Scottie hurriedly snatched up his belongings. The two lone travelers headed out to beg for food before returning to the rail yard to catch another train.

Mississippi Jungle

Just before sun up, a large group of men jumped from the freight at the yard limits. Scottie and Rod were left behind when the others disappeared into the darkness of the brush and trees.

"Bettah wait here 'til daylight," Rod said. "Then we-all can search for the hobo camp. 'Magine them guys been 'round here before the way they-all made a straight line for safety."

As they sat on the tracks waiting, Scottie finally broke the intense silence. "Do yah evah think 'bout Denva Dan?" he asked. It had been several weeks since Denver's accident and Rod was silent a couple of minutes before answering.

"Ev'ry day," Rod slowly replied with a tremor in his voice. "Can't forget a thing like that. Lawd knows I tried."

"What happened to Denva set me to thinkin'."

"'Bout what?"

"Thinkin' it shoulda been me." Scottie's voice cracked as he swallowed the lump in his throat. "I'm the one that started it by walkin' down that fool catwalk."

"Can't blame yo-self. Man made his own decision."

"Yeah, I guess. Been wondrin' if my fam'ly misses me too. It's been a while since they seen me. Thinkin' stupid things like that."

"If-n yo-all be stupid, guess I be too. Guess we both have kin someplace that we care about. Even Denva had fam'ly. Just like I got fam'ly in Texas and you got fam'ly in Rhode Island."

"Why ain't you called 'Tex' if'n you're from Texas?"

"Same reason yo-all ain't called 'Rhode' just cause you come from Rhode Island," Rod laughed. Turning serious again he said, "Made name up 'cause I was ridin' the rods. Ain't wantin' everyone to know I'm from Texas."

"Why's that? Ain't ashamed are yah?"

"Naw! Just had me some trouble in Texas and don't need to have any police questionin' me. Ain't gonna tell my secret are yah?"

"As though I had someone to tell," Scottie mumbled. Trying to be a bit more cheerful, he said, "Bet Texas is a great state."

"Nothin' but. Certain days finds me wishin' I could see my woman 'gin." Rod held his head in his hands for a few minutes. "By golly, thinks I'll be a-goin' to Texas," he said. "Would yo-all like to tag along?"

"Just be in the way ... bettah travel on alone. Your woman won't be wantin' me 'round."

"Hell, Roselle'd luv yah! We'll head to Texas soon's we catch a train headin' south." Scottie had no time to wonder if going to Texas would be a good idea. It had come up so quickly that he didn't know rightly how to respond. After he thought on it, he decided to tag along with Rod. However, he made up his mind that if he had even a hint that he wasn't wanted, he'd head back to the rails again alone.

"Where's we at now? Can you tell what state we're in?" he asked Rod.

"Sumewhere in Mississippi. That's all I know."

"Sun's up 'nuf so we bettah start lookin' for a camp," Scottie suggested as he started walking down the tracks. The familiar sound of a brook was heard off to their left. A little further on, they squatted under the low limbs of an uprooted tree to read the crude sign made from a broken box slat. Scratched into the wood was an "X" with one circle on each side. It resembled a face to Scottie. An angry one at that.

"What yah thinks that means?" He looked to Rod for an answer.

"Well, sign gives impression there's a friendly jungle down here sum'ere."

"Sure clevah puttin' sign way down there," Scottie commented. "No bulls would evah see that sign less'n they's walkin' on their knees and that ain't likely." They both laughed as they stepped across the limbs onto a path leading down through the trees.

Entering a clearing, Rod put his finger to his lips. "Best be quiet. Some's sleepin'." Scottie nodded that he had heard and quietly picked up an old cardboard from the brush and spread it between two giant roots of a shade tree. Making a bed by tucking his bundle of clothes under his head for a pillow, he rolled up in his blanket and fell asleep under the leaden sky.

****

"Caw! Caw! Caw!" Crows startled Scottie as they cried above him. With eyes heavy from sleep he looked at the black intruders perched on the wide limbs. Stretching his arms toward the sky, he yawned loudly and watched as the birds flew away in a noisy frenzy. His lower back ached from sleeping on the hard ground. Finding it impossible to get back to sleep, he stood up to rub away the stiffness.

It was spring and the sun had come up over the knoll, causing the grass to have an unusual silvery color. Fully clothed men slept on the ground, strewn about like dead soldiers on a battle field. What they owned was either on their backs or bulged from sacks and bags laying close to them. One man had an old tattered brown suitcase held shut with a rope that was tied to his waist. Because his right hand was at his belt, Scottie guessed he was clutching the handle of a knife or some other weapon to protect the old suitcase and its contents if necessary. In many cases men riding the rails mistrusted those who rode or slept near them, especially if they had anything of value.

Loud snoring came from a slender man lying on his back with his mouth gaping open. Scottie immediately recognized him as Tennessee Red for he had rode in on the same train with him. The man's red curly hair stuck out from under a cap which barely clung to the top of his head. Several layers of newspapers covered him and a brown mongrel dog lay curled up at his feet. It growled warningly as Scottie walked a little too close. Red had evidently killed the bottle of muscatel he had been nursing while riding in the boxcar. Now it lay smashed against a rock, leaving amber glass scattered over the ground.

"Don't bothah warnin' me, dog, I won't get near no stinkin' drunk," Scottie spoke gently to the dog. "How a man can sleep with bugs crawlin' 'round in his mouth I can't fig'yah," he mumbled noticing several flies finding the inside of Red's mouth to their liking. "Oh, well, it ain't none of my affair." He would like to have turned the man onto his side in case he threw up and choked, but not wanting to aggravate the mutt, he took a wide detour and headed for the brook.

Clear water bubbled and raced over the rocks. His battered metal cup was filled three times before his thirst was satisfied. Removing his shoes, he worked his way to the deepest part of the brook and stood shivering, waist deep in cold water swirling around him. Rubbing a sliver of soap over his body and clothes loosened dirt and cinders. They danced on the surface momentarily, then were carried downstream. Wading back to land, he stripped off his clothes. His body, purple from cold, was covered with goose bumps. Quickly wringing out his shirt and pants, he spread them over the tops of bushes to dry before running in circles, shaking his arms to dry himself. He stopped near a clump of bushes when he noticed a shiny object in the grass. Well, I'll be, he thought, it's a rear view mirror off of some car. He was shocked when he picked it up and looked at himself. Rubbing the stubble on his face, he said aloud, "Man, I'm a mess. Bettah find me somethin' to shave with. Look more like a bum than old Tennessee Red." Wonder what Ma would say if she could see me. Know Pa would say I turned out just like he 'spected," he said aloud. Laughing softly, he returned to his bedroll, took out his extra dry, although dirty, clothes and got dressed.

After propping the mirror in the fork of the tree above his bedroll, he picked through the smashed muscatel bottle and found a piece of glass that would make a good razor. He studied himself in the mirror while he carefully scraped his cheeks and chin until his skin was red and sore, and most of the whiskers were gone. After stuffing the mirror under the edge of the cardboard he had been lying on, he wrapped himself in his blanket and fell asleep.

His childhood nightmare returned. It seemed so real. His father was yelling and swearing at him, wildly swinging a club in his outstretched arm, and closing in on the train that Scottie was riding.

With his heart racing he jumped up at the sound of men's voices. Cold sweat beaded on his face as he looked around for Rod. He was nowhere in sight. Getting his nerves back under control, he shakily leaned against the tree and watched as the hobo jungle came to life.

"Look-ee here, boys, old Tennessee done kilt his bottle of muscatel," one man jokingly said as he looked down at the drunken man.

"Doggone flies 'ill get drunk walkin' in and out of his mouth," another chuckled. They stuffed the large stew kettle over Tennessee's face and guffawed as snores reverberated from its insides.

"Phew! Old Red's breath could kill a skunk from a mile away," another man joined in. "He's gonna have some headache when he wakes up."

"You boys had 'nuf fun! Leave the man alone!" The sudden loud command came from a very tall, muscular man who snapped the words out like a sergeant to a batch of new recruits. One man quickly snatched the kettle from Red's face.

"Yes, sah, King. Di'nt mean no harm."

"Long's you stay 'round, I'm the one yah answer to. You ain't no bettah than him. We're all a bunch of scabs on the skin of society. From now on, only thing goin' into the pot is stew -- not no man's stinkin' snores, undastand?"

Scottie was impressed with the self-proclaimed king. His long dark beard and shoulder length hair were speckled with gray. Steel gray eyes stared boldly from his tanned, weathered face. He looked like a strong and perhaps dangerous man if one should cross him. A club stuck into his belt and a knife sheathed and strapped to his leg let the others know he was not to be trifled with. This flagrant display of weapons was unheard of among the hoboes, but this man was either very confident or hankering for a fight. Scottie quietly went to the bushes, retrieved his dried clothes and got dressed. His bedroll, too, was ready for him to grab to get out of there in a moment's notice before he settled back under the oak tree.

"Thought you'd left camp," Scottie said as Rod came from behind a clump of bushes.

"Did. Looked down by edge of the watah t' see if'n any berry bushes."

"Find any?"

Rod opened his hand to show large ripened blueberries. "Shhh!" he whispered. "We'll pick 'em latah. When the skeetars dis'pear."

King had taken the coffee pot down from the tree branch where it had hung and was boiling coffee over a can of sterno. Scottie and Rod sat silently watching the men while waiting for a cup of jo.

"Coffee's ready," King announced. "Drink up. You'll be needing strength to go scrounging something to fill your bellies 'fore a night train comes through."

After Scottie finished drinking his coffee, he put his cup inside his bedroll and waited for the men to start for town.

"I been watchin' that guy over there with shiny circles on his hat," Scottie said.

"Yah mean "old feather hat" playin' cards over there?" Rod asked.

"Yeah. He's the one. Must be good at pokah. Wins every time. He's really cleanin' those men out of their goods."

"That's 'cause he's cheatin'."

"How can yah tell?"

"He ain't called Slick Willy for nothin'. Heard 'bout him before. Words 'round that he deals off the bottom of the deck.Yah bettah stay 'way from him. He's bad news."

"Three aces and two kings!" Willy hollered as he threw his cards onto the ground in front of him. "I win!"

"You couldn't have had three aces in your hand," the other man argued. "You been pulling them out of your sleeve!"

"It ain't true," Willy smiled and gestured toward the trees,"Now yah gotta pay up." The man angrily followed Willy into the woods.

"Why they goin' into the woods? Think the man has some money hid?" Scottie asked.

"Nah. Slick Willy's queer. Man probably stupid and bet his body." Rod smiled at Scottie. "Just don't get tangled up with him."

"I won't," Scottie said. "No way."

Slick Willy

96

A Sacrificial Lamb

"Slick Willy," King commanded, "you and the boy get meat for stew. Rest of you men get what yah can."

"Think ye're man 'nuf to find meat?" The raspy voice behind Scottie startled him. Lurching forward and jumping to his feet, he turned and faced a grinning Slick Willy. The man's appearance didn't fit his voice. He was thin, with a hairy face and glistening dark eyes that made Scottie slightly uncomfortable. Pulled down on Willy's forehead was a broad-brimmed black hat with a band surrounded by shiny silver circles. He winked at Scottie and whispered, "You're one cute kid."

"I'm not a kid!" Scottie replied angrily.

"We're to get meat!" the guttural voice continued. His tone would have intimidated Scottie a few months ago, but he had learned how to fake confidence. He bravely looked into the dark eyes that reminded him of his father's and said, "I'm comin'. Be right with yah." Although ordinarily no hobo stole from another, Scottie still did not feel comfortable with this particular group of men. Hurrying out of sight with his bedroll, he placed it on the ground under a leafy bush and covered it with leaves. Knowing that he might be watched, he stepped from behind the trees, buttoning the fly of his pants, and boldly walked over to Slick Willy and stated, "Let's head out."

Rambling along the back road to town, they passed farms where horses grazed and cows huddled together under shade trees. A few sheep and lambs bunched against a cool rocky wall next to the road eyed them cautiously and suspiciously sniffed the air. Scottie reached over the wall and gently ran his hands through the soft warm wool of a lamb. It felt like soft rabbit's fur to his hands that were used to cold winds and hard metal of the trains. Slick Willy angrily motioned him to get coming so he ran to catch up and fell in beside him.

In town they found their way to the back door of a meat market. A short fat man with a blood stained apron tied around his plump belly stood with meat cleaver in hand. He glanced up with distrustful eyes and then continued his work. The stench of rancid fat and wet feathers from freshly plucked chickens was sickening. Scottie's stomach tightened at the smell of chicken guts lumped together in a bucket at the man's feet.

"What's the matter?" Slick Willy said. "You're a man. Go ahead and knock." Scottie tapped on the door, but if it hadn't been for Slick Willy's insolent look, he would have run from the sights and smells which made him want to puke.

"How's 'bout piece of meat you can't sell?" Slick Willy's hoarse voice pleaded. "Even if'n it ain't too good a piece. We need to eat. Please mister?"

The butcher's eyes set like two lumps of coal in his angry flushed face made Scottie cautiously step back away from the building. He wished Slick Willy would stop pleading and just come away from the door.

"If it's work you're wanting, they're hiring in the fields down the road. If it's free meat you're wanting, you'll not get it here!" the man shouted, raising his cleaver threateningly. "Get down the road before I get the police on yah!"

"Damn you!" Slick Willy growled, kicking the side of the building and thumbing his nose at the butcher.

"That man sure was somethin'," Scottie said as they hurried to the outskirts of town. "Those chicken guts smelled worse than any man that's been on the rails without a bath for a year."

"Know what yah mean," Willy smirked. "I was hoping we'd be able to get ahold of those guts. Then I could chuck them stinkin' innards back into his fat face."

They continued to take turns knocking on doors. The housewives either didn't answer or, standing behind locked screen doors, told them they had nothing for them. Heavy wooden doors were slammed in their faces.

"We're not headin' back without meat," Slick Willy said.

"Whatcha gonna do? Kill one of these dogs that's nippin' at our heels?"

"Nope. Gotta plan. We'll get us a lamb."

"Yah thinkin' 'bout those sheep we saw, ain't yah? We got nothin' to kill it with," Scottie said, hoping to discourage him from stealing one of the sheep. "We gonna take it back to camp blattin' and kickin'?"

"Don't need no knife, boy. Just need to be creative."

As they briskly retraced their steps down the dirt road, Scottie wondered what Slick Willy had in mind.

"Yeah, lamb would sure be tasty," Slick Willy's gravelly voice was almost inaudible as it rumbled in his throat. Guess he's talkin' to himself, Scottie thought for the man continued to mumble as they hurried toward the sheep that were still huddled in the shade of the wall.

"Bet yah I can catch one of those wooly beasts with my bare hands," Slick Willy boasted.

"Bet yah can't," Scottie said, confident the sheep would run away.

"Hold my hat," Willy said tossing it toward Scottie. "Give a holler if yah see anyone comin'. Don't forget our bet!"

Slick Willy crawled over the stone wall downwind of the sheep. Slowly, he slithered over the grass like a cat hunting a mouse. His eyes focused on the sheep which were studying Scottie, unaware of the predator closing in. Flicking out his arm as quick as a lizard's tongue catching a fly, Slick grasped the back leg of a lamb. Its loud bleating panicked the other sheep and they dashed away across the field. Slick Willy swiftly jumped the stone wall and ran across the road into the woods, dragging the bleating, struggling animal with him. Scottie was close on his heels.

"Get a rock! Hit it in the head with a rock!" Slick Willy shouted as he excitedly held the lamb on the ground.

Shuffling through the leaves, Scottie came up with a rock the size of a baseball. Holding it tightly in his two hands, he closed his eyes and smashed the lamb's head as hard as he could. Stunned, and with blood running from its forehead, it fell limply to the ground.

"Smash it again!" Slick screeched. "Before it gets up!" Scottie whacked its head two more times to make sure it was dead and not suffering. Slick Willy had pulled a straight razor from his pocket and it snapped open with a quick movement of his wrist. After running the blade across the bloody rock a few times, he slit the lamb's throat and jumped back, laughing as the blood streamed out.

Straight Razor

"Grab hold this critter while I cut it!" he hollered to Scottie. Hacking at it with the razor, he tore off the hind quarter.

"You're turnin' gray in the face, Scottie. Stomach feelin' squeamish?" Slick Willy laughed.

"No. It don't botha me. Aftah all, gotta eat," Scottie replied, turning his head away from the gore covering the animal's wool.

Carrying the lamb's hind quarter, Slick Willy charged down the road, leaving the rest of the carcass for the wild animals.

When they entered camp with the ragged chunk of meat, King's steel gray eyes turned as dark as a thunder cloud. He stared at Slick Willy from under the brim of his cap.

"Don't know where yah got this, Slick, but I can guess. We best move our camp up the tracks a ways. Police will be coming. You've left a bloody trail right to our camp." He turned and shouted, "Got to move camp men!"

Scottie scooted for his bedroll in the bushes. The rest of the men hurriedly doused the fire and grabbed their stuff. King wrapped his shirt around the handle of the stew pot and poured the boiling water onto the ground. He ran with the hot kettle half full of vegetables held at arm's length. Moving rapidly, the men sprinted up the tracks before veering off into the woods. They didn't stop running until King found an opening in the trees that he considered suitable.

"Guess these veg'tables cooked 'nuf," King said as he set the kettle on a flat rock. Pulling his knife from its sheath, he tossed it to Slick Willy, and commanded, "Get the meat cleaned and ready for cookin' while we make a fire." Slick picked up the knife and motioned for Scottie to help him. By the time the meat was skinned and scraped, a roaring fire blazed in the middle of the clearing. The lamb quarter, stuck on a spit made from a green sapling, was held over the fire by two forked branches. Flames licked the meat like red tongues and grease spattered, exploding on the logs, and making a dark spiral of smoke rise in a column through the tree tops. While they waited for the meat, the men wolfed down the half raw vegetables from the pot.

To pass the time, an older man called Whitey pulled a harmonica from his pocket. His fringe of white hair fluttered as he bobbed his head and his body swayed with the rhythm as he stomped out the time with his boot. Playing the old railroad songs like *"She'll Be Coming 'Round the Mountain When She Comes"* and *"I've Been Workin' On the*

Railroad, " he awkwardly hopped around in a happy dance of his own making. His cheerfulness was contagious. Soon the men were singing *"The Music Goes 'Round and 'Round"* and *"You Must Have Been A Beautiful Baby."* Scottie sang lustier than the rest as he tried to keep the men in tune. One of the men tried to teach them the Lindy Hop, which ended up more like an Indian wardance than anything else. They swung each other wildly around as they danced and sang to Whitey's tunes. Scottie couldn't remember ever having such a carefree happy time at a jungle before.

When the meat was cooked, King sliced off a chunk for himself; then each man took a share. Scottie chewed slowly, forcing the meat down his throat. The remembrance of the lamb's terrified eyes brought back memories of his brother and sisters peering out from under the furniture at the violence in his home. These thoughts forced their way into his head without warning. How he wished he could just forget his family. He wondered why the only happy times he remembered as a child were riding the trains and running barefoot on the beach in Pensacola, Florida. These brief episodes seldom surfaced, while his father's cruelty remained a large part of his life that haunted him with nighmares. His usual answer to forgetting these thoughts was to keep moving. Keeping his mind active with schemes for action kept him alive.

"Rod, how 'bout goin' back and waitin' for the train, and maybe pickin' those blueberries?" Scottie asked. Rod nodded as they gathered up their bedrolls and prepared to head back toward the hobo jungle from which they had run a few hours before.

"Where yah headed?" Slick Willy asked Scottie. "Don't forget yah made a bet with me and yah lost. I expect payment."

"Leave the boy alone or answer to me," Rod said, shoving Slick Willy aside. "He ain't givin' yah nothin', understand?"

"I'll find yah alone sometime boy," Willy uttered.

When Scottie and Rod got to the camp it was deserted. A flattened coffee pot and ashes where cardboards and clothing had been piled and burned was evidence that someone had intentionally destroyed the camp.

"We bettah get at those berries and then git outta here," Rod said, "'fore police return."

Heading downstream a ways they reached the bushes heavy with ripened clusters of swamp blueberries. Hastily eating their fill, they swished water in their mouth to get the blue stain off their teeth and headed to the freight yard to wait. Rod sat silently on the end of a railroad tie while Scottie paced back and forth.

"Sit down," Rod said. "Have a cig'rette." Holding out his half-smoked fag, he murmured, "Yo-all makin' me nervous."

"Sorry," Scottie said as he took the butt and sat down.

"Whatcha thinkin' anyhow?" Rod asked.

"Oh, 'bout my fam'ly. Ev'ry once in a while wonder how they's doin'."

"Hobo jungle's your home now. Yo-all hafta take care of yah-self. They's all right. Betta off'n yo-all. At least they got a roof over their head." After a few minutes of silence, Rod continued, "Hope the next train is headin' south. I guess I'm a-gettin' homesick too."

"Here come the men." Scottie nodded toward the group of stragglers.

"Bettah join them," Rod said. They stood and watched the group of hoboes as they sought the cover of bushes where they could safely watch for an evening train.

A brakeman looking over the yards

Layover in Texas

Just as Rod had hoped, the next train was headed south. It took them near Fort Worth, Texas to a yard where railroad bulls roamed with guns in belts and billy clubs in hands.

"Looks doubtful we can hop this 'un," Scottie said as he studied the train. "There's no empty or unlocked boxcar."

"We can hop 'er. 'Twas our luck to get a train headin' to Texas. This train'll take me where I want to go. Yo-all stay behind 'n catch next train if'n you want. No hard feelin's."

"I'll go with yah," Scottie said. "Where's we gonna ride?"

"On the catwalk of the tanka."

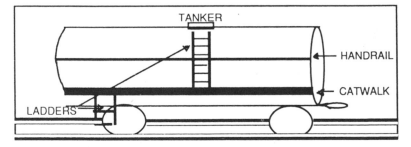

"Sure we can make it?" Scottie asked, skeptically looking at the narrow metal catwalk running the length of the tanker. "We'd be seen by the bulls ridin' in the open like that."

"Look at those stupid guys," Rod said as he pointed at the train. Tennessee Red, clutching his mongrel dog, was climbing the back ladder to the top of a boxcar with Slick Willy following him. When they got to the roof, they lay flat and wormed their way forward. The railroad bulls fired a few rounds into the air and roared with laughter as the two men slid to the ground and scurried back to the cover of the

103

brush.

"Bulls are sure poor shots," Rod laughed.

"Good thing or Tennessee and Slick Willy'd be dead by now," Scottie snickered.

"They just ain't got it up here," Rod said as he pointed to his head. "Tennessee prob'ly still half soused and Willy there just gamblin' with his life. Just follah my lead and we won't get caught 'cause I've got a trick up my sleeve."

"I'm with yah whatever the scheme is."

"Soon's train starts, run for the tanka. Get to the catwalk quick and hang on for your life." Scottie looked skeptically at the catwalk on the tanker. It ran the length of the car about three feet from the ground. The hand rail was several feet above that. It would take the concentration of a tight rope walker to keep their balance when the train picked up speed. It seemed like a fool thing to do for they would be exposed to gun fire if detected, but to a sixteen year old it was exciting and daring and doable.

The bulls had gone to the other side of the train. Scottie and Rod waited behind a large tree trunk. They watched the train with their faces pressed tightly against the rough bark, ready to duck at the slightest shadow.

"Go!" Rod whispered as the rods slid back and forth pumping the big wheels forward. Scottie ran with his upper body bent as low to the ground as he could. Grabbing a rung of the ladder, he swung himself onto the catwalk. He wrapped his legs and arms around the narrow metal walk to keep himself from being thrown by the lurching of the train as it slowly left the rail yard. Holding his breath, he slipped his body upward until he could balance on the catwalk and grab for the handrail. Only after his heart stopped racing did he dare turn his head to see if Rod had made it. He made eye contact and grinned at the man pressed against the tanker with the wind wildly flapping his shirt tail.

Scottie's hands grew numb from cold as the train picked up speed. The full realization of the danger he was in hit him like a hammer. He knew if he lost his grip he would be thrown onto the gravel bed or under the wheels. Gripping the metal rail tightly with one hand, he used the other hand to quickly fasten himself to the hand rail with a loop made from his pants belt. With this added security, he could stuff one hand at a time in his pocket; all the while keeping himself against the tanker so that the wind couldn't get between his body and the curved metal.

Darkness settled around them. The wind whipped and tugged at their bodies with gale force. While the train rumbled through the countryside, Scottie tried to forget his fear by keeping his mind busy thinking about Oscar, his father's mule. How that son of a gun could kick and buck! He remembered amusing his sister by running up to Oscar when he was grazing and jumping onto his back. Each time, the mule would take off at a gallop with Scottie hanging to its neck for dear life. Most generally he got thrown off and Oscar went racing across the field, kicking out with his hind legs. Pa would've thumped me good if he knew I rode that old mule.

"Leave me the hell alone!" he shouted with frustration into the whistling wind. Although he was physically away from his Pa, memories were strange things. They rattled around in his brain just waiting to surface and torment him. And right now he didn't want to think of the past. He had enough problems here and now.

Scottie sadly turned his eyes toward Rod. The man who had treated him as an equal and a friend would soon be separated from him. A lump came to his throat. He tried to convince himself that Rod meant nothing to him. Just a hobo who had let him hang with him for a while. Rod had a right to go home if he wanted; none of his business. It would be painful to say goodbye, but once he'd left Rod in Texas, he'd take care of himself. Nobody else cared about him, he was sure of that. He was going to have to make it on his own in this lonely world.

His only hope was that his friend Floyd hadn't forgotten him. To cheer himself up he thought of the day he would march up to Floyd and tell him how he'd ridden a swaying tanker thundering over the tracks at 100 m.p.h. When Scottie was a kid, he had stood outside the gate and watched other boys ride the ferris wheel and merry-go-round, but this ride was more exciting. He had lived through things that the boys back home couldn't even imagine.

Rod's dark silhouette was way toward the front of the tanker now. The train seemed to have slowed down so Scottie worked his way forward by sliding the safety belt loop along the hand rail and dragging his feet up the narrow catwalk.

"Get ready to jump!" Rod yelled when Scottie got close enough to hear. Scottie was caught off guard when Rod reached down by the couplings under his feet and disconnected the air hoses. Compressed air screeched as it escaped from the hoses. The train stopped with a jolt. Scottie and Rod were thrown to the ground where they scrambled for a foothold in the sliding gravel. The boxcars to the rear of the tanker rolled into the ones ahead of them with thunderous whacks.

"What the hell happened?!!" someone shouted.

"Who cut the brakes?!!"

Lanterns flitted like lightning bugs against the darkened sky as the railroad bulls and brakemen ran from car to car, searching for the culprit. The curses of frustrated men, the cry of a hobo thrown off the train, and general noise and confusion filled the night air. Scottie's heart pounded as he raced toward the sound of Rod's feet stomping through a cornfield. An unexpected wire fence knocked the wind out of him and sent him flying to the ground. As soon as he got his breath back, he climbed the fence and continued running. Rod was waiting for him on the other side of the field.

"Nevah seen anythin' like that," Scottie said as the train started down the tracks. "Sure threw them into a riot when you pulled the air hose."

"Had them a-huslin' some," Rod laughed. "Don't want to get caught doin' that trick though. Bulls catch yah messin' with the brakes and yo'all'll end up in jail for dang sure."

"Guess no harm was done. Less'n, 'course, they left half the train sittin' on the tracks," Scottie snickered.

"Sho 'nuf shook 'em up some." Rod said. They both bent over with laughter, relieved to be off the tanker safely and satisfied that a trick had been pulled on the railroad company. Rod wiped the tears from his eyes and sweat from his face. "Almost home. Let's git started."

Approaching a small shack at the edge of the cornfield, Scottie stepped back as two dogs bounded toward them, barkly loudly. When Rod called them by name, they stealthily walked around them, sniffing at their pants legs.

"Roselle, it's me! Horace!" Rod hollered. A thin woman appeared, silhouetted in the doorway by a kerosene lamp glowing behind her. Rod ran to her, wrapped her in his arms, and kissed her. He shoved the dogs aside with his foot as they joyfully jumped up and tried to lick his face.

Feeling awkwardly aware of his intrusion on this scene, Scottie stood to the side and watched the stars. He was still mulling over the events of the evening when Rod called his name.

Rod balanced on the couplings and got ready to turn the brake rod.

"Scottie, come on over and meet Roselle. Roselle, this is a young friend of mine. Came to visit yo-all."

"Any friend of Horace's is a friend of mine. Yo-all come on in. Ain't got much to offer, but what I have yo-all are more than welcome to it."

Inside the small interior was a combination kitchen and living room which ran the length of the shack. Walls separated two smaller rooms at the back of the house. It was similar to the No. 3 shack Scottie's family had lived in when he was a kid in Alabama. The only difference was it had floors and windows that made it look more like a home. A kerosene lamp sat on the table and lit the center of the room. The other furniture, consisting of an overstuffed couch and chair and a victrola, sat in the shadows.

Scottie slyly looked at Rod and asked, "Should I call yah Rod or Horace?"

"Rod!" Roselle exclaimed. "Where'd yo-all git that name from?"

"It's what we called him on the rails, M'am." Scottie studied the toe of his shoe as he murmured, "Thought it was his name. Told us it was." He looked out of the corner of his eye at Rod and smiled.

"Yeah, like your name is Scottie," Rod said with a grin. "No one ridin' the rails uses their right name; no one cares what your name is. They calls yah whatevah yah look like or act like. They don't want to know nothin' 'bout yah anyway."

"Well, yo-all keep callin' him Rod. He nevah liked the name Horace no-how," Roselle said as she waved her hand in dismissal of the subject.

Roselle radiated with happiness. Her wavy auburn hair shone with reddish highlights making a full and beautiful frame around her face. Her blue eyes came alive as she looked lovingly at Rod. Scottie thought she was a beautiful woman in spite of dark circles under her eyes.

"Where's my mannahs? Yo-all must be starved."

"Plenty hungry t'night, Rose," Rod nodded as he wearily sunk into the faded blue overstuffed couch that sagged practically to the floor under his weight. His eyes hungrily followed Roselle's movements as she took a small piece of salt pork and a pan of cold grits out of the ice box.

"It'll be ready shortly," she said. She chopped the pork into little pieces and dumped them into a frying pan. "I'll make yah gravy to pour over the grits. Yah always liked that." As the pork sizzled in the pan, she turned to look at Rod and sighed, "Cain't believe yo-all really here. Times I thought I'd nevah see yah ag'in."

"Yo-all know'd I'd be back," Rod said. "The law was just gettin' too close to my tail for runnin' moonshine. Had to dis'pear 'til things cooled down. Yo-all knowed I couldn't stay away forevah. Yo-all undastand, don't yah, Roselle?" Rod pleaded with her. "Yo-all undastand, don't yah, that I had to take off in the night like I did?"

"I guess. Was mad and sad for a while, but I'm bein' mighty glad yo-all here now." After a moment of silence, she stirred the pork and added mischievously, "I ain't been alone, though." From the look on Rod's face, Scottie knew Roselle had gotten even with him for leavin' her like he had.

"Who's livin' with yah?!" Rod jumped to his feet. "Yah went and got yo-self 'nother man?"

"Roselle tilted her head to the side and gazed at him with half-closed eyelids. "Had to have someone to keep revenuas away." As Rod paced back and forth in front of the couch, Scottie kept himself occupied by watching the cockroaches running across the floor.

"It's your cousin Herman," Roselle laughed. "Been stayin' in the back room. Yo-all should see your face. Makes me proud to think yo-all worried like that." She lightly patted his arm. "Yo-all will always be my man."

"Warn't worried a bit," Rod commented as he plunked back into the warped seat of the couch. "Herm's harmless 'nuf. Ol' humpback in back room now?"

"Naw. He's out on the town. Be in latah." As she stirred the flour into the pork grease, she said, "Scottie'll be beddin' down in Herm's room. Ain't no other space."

"That'll be fine. He's slept with worse." Rod grinned at Scottie. "Yo-all don't mind sleepin' in same room with Herm, does yah?"

"Suits me fine. Long's Herm doesn't care."

"Course not," Roselle replied firmly. "Herm won't care."

While Roselle was looking in Scottie's direction, Rod reached into his overall pocket.

"Brought yah somethin' real pretty, Rosie honey," Rod said as he held out a small package wrapped in newspaper. As she folded back the paper, Scottie could see it was a colorful Little Orphan Annie button.

"It's beaut'ful. Real beaut'ful, Horace ... I mean Rod." Her face

glowed in the lamplight as she lovingly held
the pin as though it was a lump of gold.

"Bless yah. This is so pretty. Whose the
little girl?"

"Orphan Annie. See it says right here."
He pointed to the lettering at the top of the
button.

"Oh," she whispered and her cheeks turned red as she stared at the
printed name. Scottie felt her embarrassment at not being able to read.
She ought not to be ashamed he thought. He was thankful he had at least
four years of schooling. It sure must be hard on a person not to be able
to read signs and names of food on boxes and such.

"Been pickin' up buttons here and there," Rod laughed noticing
how uncomfortable she was. He pointed to his overalls and ran his
fingers across the pins hanging on the top of his overalls. "None of them
pretty like that one. Knew I had to save it for my Rosie. It's practic'ly
new. Been keepin' it in my shirt next to my heart so's it wouldn't get a
scratch on it. You always lis'ened to Little Orphan Annie on the radio.
Knew you'd love this pin."

"I always did love list'nin' to the girl and her dog Sandy. Can't hear
her much now. Radio done broke. Thank you for rememberin'." As
Roselle pinned the button to her dress, Scottie noticed tears in her eyes.
Sure thinks she's got a treasure, he thought. Can't imagine anyone
that thrilled over a pin Rod found on the ground.

Roselle's show of emotion made Scottie uncomfortable. Suddenly
feeling closed in and confined, he fiddled nervously and picked at
cotton bursting from the arm of the overstuffed chair. He felt like an
intruder. Rod's homecoming should have been more private.

"Maybe I best be leavin'," Scottie suggested. The dogs at Rod's feet
perked up their ears and wagged their tails.

"Naw," Rod said. "Dogs say diff'rent. Can't send a friend into the
darkness alone tonight. We'll make room for yah." The dog named
Jack came and lay his head on Scottie's lap and watched him with dark
inquiring eyes. Its bushy tail swept the floor as it wagged back and
forth. The other dog, Butch, obviously favored Rod. He lay contendedly
across the man's feet and faked sleeping, occasionally rolling one eye
upward to assure himself that Rod was still there. That is one ugly dog,
Scottie thought, for Butch's nose was like a black piece of leather

bunched up and stuck on with such force that it squished the dog's face flat. Never had he seen a dog like that in all his travels. Even its mouth was ugly with its long protruding teeth. Scottie patted Jack's head, happy that this dog liked him and not the homely one. While stroking the dog's head, he listened to Rod stretch the truth about his adventures on the rails. Roselle looked mighty impressed as she kept turning away from the stove to look at Rod. The aroma of pork frying and coffee steaming smelled so good that Scottie's stomach rumbled.

"Time to eat," Roselle said as she placed the fried grits smothered with gravy beside a pot of hot coffee on the table. This simple meal tasted better than a banquet to the famished boy.

"Thank yah, Ma'm, for such a nice meal," Scottie said politely. "Sure nice of yah to be willin' to share."

"Yo-all welcome," Roselle said as she rested her chin on her arm and stared at Scottie. He was conscious of her eyes on him and he felt the hot blood making his face red as he scraped at the bits of food left on his plate.

"What made a boy like yo-self take to ridin' the trains?" she asked.

Scottie remained silent while memories of home slid through his mind like gummy molasses, picking up every unhappy and ugly thought he had of his homelife. Finally he murmured, "Had to git away from my old man."

"Don't be askin' the boy questions," Rod said. "He's tuckered out and needin' sleep."

"I'm sorry," Roselle gently laid her hand on Scottie's arm. "Didn't mean nothin'."

"It's okay. Would yah like help with the dishes?" he blurted out. His hands shook as he hastily picked up the plates. Being touched so gently by a woman shook his whole insides. The plates clattered together as he set them in the sink.

"We don't need no help. Rod and me'll handle the dishes," Roselle said gently. "Yo-all best get some sleep." She motioned for him to follow her into the small bedroom. A cot, kitchen chair, and a couple of orange crates overflowing with clothes were the only furnishings.

"Yo-all can sleep comfort'ble on this quilt," Roselle said as she yanked it off the cot and folded it to make a bed in the corner.

"I don't wanta take Herman's quilt 'way from him."

"He won't even notice. Too hot for 'im to sleep under anyway."

Scottie was too tired to argue. Sinking onto the soft quilt, he whispered "Thank yah" as Roselle turned to leave.

Jack had followed them into the room and curled up at Scottie's feet. Somehow the closeness of the dog was comforting to him, not at all like the feelings he had when Roselle touched his arm. Closing his eyes, he thought how nice it was that Rod had a loving woman like Roselle waiting for him.

****

The sun streaming in the small window signaled daybreak. Scottie studied the room; it looked very small and cluttered. Jack was still curled up next to him so he gently nudged the dog aside and raised himself to peek over the window ledge. He didn't notice Jack slipping out the door.

"Well, ain't that somethin'," he said aloud. "We're practic'ly sittin' in the middle of the corn fields." The fields of tall green corn stalks stretched outta sight and still kept going. Men and women with loose clothing and broad-brimmed hats worked their way up the rows. Stuffing the ears of corn into bags, they called back and forth to each other in friendly tones.

Standing to stretch and get the stiffness out of his back, Scottie noticed the cot was rumpled. Herman must have slept in here and I didn't even take note, he thought. Funny, if I'd been on the rails or in a jungle, no one would have gotten close to me without my knowing it. Must have been more tired than I thought.

"Wants breakfas', boy?" Rod said. He stood in the doorway smiling and scratching his head. "Guess Roselle and Herm workin' the fields. Left us to git our own grub."

"Nevah refuse anythin' to eat," Scottie said. Starting to pull his tattered shoes over his socks he asked, "Where's the outhouse?"

"Just follow path 'round the house." Rod motioned.

"Hi boys," Scottie said as he went outside. "Hot ain't it?" Shielding his eyes against the sun, he walked over to pet the two dogs. Their tongues were hanging almost to the ground as they stretched out in the shade of a small shrub near the house.

Sitting over the hole on the board seat in the outhouse was a luxury to Scottie. For months he had squatted behind some bush or hung his rear over a log when nature called. He swatted the many flies buzzing around him as he thumbed through the Sears & Roebuck catalog used for toilet paper. The pages with women wearing corsets and pantaloons were studied with a good deal of interest.

By the time he got back to the house, scrambled eggs and fried bread were on the table and the aroma of fresh coffee filled the small shack.

"You're sure a good cook," Scottie said while scraping the last few crumbs from his plate.

"Ain't nothin' to it. Just crack the eggs and pan does the rest."

"Do yah think I should take a train out tonight?" Scottie asked Rod after a few minutes of silently thinking. "Know I can't stay here forevah. Maybe I bettah catch a train out tonight."

"Stay long's yo-all like. Rosie and Jack likes yah and," Rod laughed, "guess I can stand yo-all a few days."

"What 'bout Herman? Think he minds someone in his room? Slept so sound didn't even hear 'im come in las' night."

"He came in late, but went to work pickin' corn first thing this mornin'," Rod said as he dug at his head again and said reflectively, "Tomorrah she'll be wantin' me to work, I s'pose."

"I picked cotton before," Scottie said with enthusiasm, "when I was only eight years old. Guess I could try pickin' corn for my keep. But only for a few days," he quickly added. "Gotta leave here 'fore long. Train ridin' in my blood."

"Go whenevah yah feel the urge, but we ain't pushin' yah."

Rod and Scottie worked in silence clearing away dishes and tidying up before they sat a spell.

"Did yah evah put the rig on someone and have them give yah somethin' bad to eat?" Scottie asked. Rod looked up, still running his tongue across the paper on the fag he was rolling. Handing the makin's to Scottie, he looked at the boy as though he didn't really know what he was asking.

"Sometimes pretty bad stuff, but I swollered it some how. Why'd yo-all ask a question like that?"

"Just thinkin'. A real mean woman just popped into my head," Scottie said as he slowly tapped tobacco into the cigarette paper.

"Well, what's 'bout this woman? Whatcha gets from her?"

"It's a long story."

"We ain't goin' nowhere. Let's hear it."

"One day while you was sleepin' in a jungle in Mississippi, thought

113

I'd try on my own to put the rig on someone." Scottie hesitated as he remembered all too well the winding dirt driveway, the neat white farmhouse, and the woman with pinched hardened features and eyes full of hatred who had opened the door and glared at him. "Woman hollered at me," he continued, "to get out of there 'fore she sicced her dog on me. Told me to get a job or go home where I belonged. I can still remember the door slammin' in my face. Course I was mad as hell." Scottie slowly dragged on his cigarette and let the smoke drift from his mouth before he continued. "Then she calls me back. Told me she had found somethin' for me. She handed me a brown bag as nice as you please and warned me not to open it 'til I got out to the road. I grabbed the bag and high-tailed it down the driveway. I was 'specting her to send her dog after me."

"What'd she give yah?" Rod asked when Scottie didn't continue right away.

"The mean old witch done give me a crumpled up cupcake mixed in with dirt, hair, and floor sweepin's."

Rod shook his head in disbelief and sympathy.

"She was pure mean through and through," Scottie said. "I was almost in tears from hunger and frustration as I dragged back to camp. I truly was stirred up with hatred for her."

"Mustn't let people like that turn yo-all bittah, Scottie. Forget 'em and go on with life. 'Sides, I likes yah to keep that lop-sided grin on yah face," Rod teased as he lightly tapped him on the jaw.

"Bein' awake durin' the day makin' me sleepy. Think I'll take a nap," Scottie said. He was annoyed that he had shared this story with Rod, especially the part about him feeling like crying. Made him look like a boy instead of a man.

"Yeah, sure breaks the routine of sleepin' days and ridin' nights. Guess we-all both needs rest. Got to pick corn tomorr-ee."

As Scottie plunked down on the quilt in the corner, a train's whistle wailed out its lonesome call. Homesickness grabbed his guts and twisted his insides into knots. He wondered if anyone back home missed him. Maybe his Ma worried about him, but he could picture his Pa delirious with happiness that he wasn't around. Then another thought popped into his head. Suppose the family had moved because they couldn't pay the rent? What if he couldn't find them again? Finally he came up with an image of his Pa slaving away to support the family

114

and wishing he had some help from his oldest son. That idea made him feel better.

"Hell. I don't want to think 'bout what might be happenin' back in Rhode Island," he muttered. "Got my own problems to work out." He lay with his hands behind his head and imagined what the next town would be like and how soon he could get out of this house and back to the rails. With his head full of thoughts of catching the next train, his family slowly slipped in and out of his dreams like shapes in the fog as he slept most of the day.

****

"Yo-all goin' to Pie Auction tomorrah night?" A deep voice jolted Scottie awake. Jumping to his feet, he awkwardly faced the man standing in the middle of the room.

"You H-h-herman?" Scottie stuttered as he tried to remember the man's name.

"That's me," Herman laughed. "Gave yah a start did I?"

Herman was shorter than Scottie with a broad chest and muscular upper arms. His lower body was a contrast; his long legs gave the impression that they met at his waistline. He had a handsome face with well proportioned features and a broad smile that made Scottie like him immediately.

"Supper'll be ready shortly," he said. As he turned to leave, Scottie noticed how the man limped. His twisted spine caused his back to extend out like a wedge under his shirt. No wonder Rod called him "hump back" he thought, but that still seemed like a cruel name.

"Tomorrah night, I'll take yah to the Pie Auction," Herman said as he stuck his head back around the door casing.

"Well, okay," Scottie answered. "Sounds good ... Yeah." He waited until Herman was out of ear shot before he muttered, "If'n I'm still here that is."

Scottie felt guilty as he ate supper because the meager chicken looked too small for four people. He ate only one slice of the breast and filled up on greens and corn.

"Yo-all will like the Pie Auction," Herman looked at Scottie and smiled.

"What they do at a Pie Auction? 'Sides auctionin' off pies I mean," Scottie asked.

115

"We-all have a dance and gets to meet the girls in town."

"Yeah," Rod added as he winked as Scottie, "might find a girl-friend." Scottie blushed. As good as that sounded, what girl would want him with his dirty ragged clothes? None of them would want to dance with me, he thought. Can't dance anyway.

"Last year we had real fun," Roselle commented. "Real good lookin' man bought my apple pie." She looked at Rod impishly. "We danced all evenin'."

"Yo-all tryin' to make me jealous ag'in, Roselle?"

"Well, just tellin' what happened. Ask Herman. Ain't it the truth, Herm?"

"Shore 'nuf. Roselle had a grand time."

Rod shoved his chair back and angrily stalked out the door. Scottie was surprised that she had gotten Rod so upset. Didn't think a little thing like that should get a man so disturbed.

"Well, guess I bettah go tell Rod I'm sorry," Roselle said after waiting a few minutes to see if he would come back inside.

"Lovers!" Herman said with a shrug. "Glad I got me no steady woman."

"Think I'll go to bed," Scottie said as he placed his dishes in the sink.

Sitting alone in the bedroom, he thought again that he should not have come here. He had slept all day and wasn't a bit tired. He'd be lying awake all night listenin' for a train whistle. Well, Pie Auction or not, he wasn't going to stay any longer. His bedroll was soon ready. He never liked saying goodbyes, so he took a stub of a pencil and a piece of scrap paper and wrote, "Thank you. Good luck to you, Scottie." While placing the note on Herman's cot he noticed a sheathed knife covered with dust under the chair. Rationalizing that no one would miss it, he grabbed it, stuck it into his belt, and stealthily climbed out the window and into the night.

He could hear Rod and Roselle arguing as he slipped through the corn field and out to the rails.

A Dog Named "Bo"

Now that Scottie had safely worked his way through the cornfield, he stood like a wild animal freed from its cage. Long railroad tracks disappeared into the dark countryside in both directions. Without a clue which way to go, he plunked down on the ground Indian style and gazed at the full moon and star-filled sky.

His happiness at being away from the confines of the small shack was dwindling as he thought of Rod. Memories marched through his mind like soldiers on parade. The man had been kind to him, taught him survival in this depressing world and he deserved a proper good-bye, but Scottie knew that was impossible. He would not go back and make a blubbering fool of himself. Staying longer at Roselle's house wasn't wise; he had to get on with his life alone. "Yes, sir, no ties to nobody and that's the way I want it," he stated aloud.

A train whistle could be heard in the distance. It was like a familiar voice telling him the direction to take. He jumped up and started out. Gravel crunched under his feet as he trudged along beside the rails. When a coyote howled off to his right, he hastily hitched his bedroll higher on his shoulder and held tightly to its rope as a shiver went up his spine.

Dark inky clouds scudded across the moon and flung out like a blanket covering the stars. Squinting into the darkness, he hurried along. His toe slammed against a railroad tie making him trip and fall. Landing flat on his belly in the gravel bed, he lay motionless, with his heart beating wildly as something moved through the rustling dry grass close beside him. Fear of what he could not see caused him to slowly reach for the knife he had stolen from Herman. Holding his arm high and tensed in readiness to fight whatever was coming his way, he took in long, slow, deep breaths.

117

The silhouette of an animal came within two feet of his face. Although barely able to make out the white stripe down its back and the large bushy tail, his nose told him it was a skunk. Quietly he slid his face down into the gravel just in case it decided to spray. Although the animal ignored him and disappeared into the brush at the other side of the tracks, Scottie lay tensely holding the knife high in readiness until his arm grew numb. Raising his head slightly, he peered into the darkness until he was convinced that the skunk was gone. Only then did he let his arm drop. After taking several deep breaths, he slowly pushed himself to his feet. With shaking hands he returned the knife to its sheath at his belt and hurried on with his search for a freight yard or hobo jungle.

****

Over the months darkness had become Scottie's friend, for he learned there was safety when you could not be seen. Tonight, for the first time since running away from home, he felt uncommonly lonely for human company. He thrust thoughts of home to the back of his mind. He pushed on, happy that a breeze had swept the dark clouds further east letting the moon shine dimly on the rails again. Concentrating on his journey, he didn't notice a dog approaching until its barking startled him. Looking over his shoulder at the dark shape running toward him, he instinctively squatted and picked up a handful of gravel and stones and threw it in the animal's direction.

"Git!" he hollered. The dog yipped and ran back out of range. Then it slowly hunkered down and crawled toward him again.

"Git! Go home! Dog! Git!" he yelled. The dog bolted and ran several yards down the tracks but kept his eyes trained on the boy. The minute Scottie started walking, the dog trotted up behind him and sniffed his leg.

"Stupid dog," Scottie muttered, "why don't yah git away from me?" Hoping to leave the dog behind, he flailed his arms and started running. From over his shoulder he could see the silhouette of the dog sitting on the tracks with his hind leg lifted, scratching the underside of his belly. Good, Scottie thought, while he's scratching maybe he'll remember to get himself back home. But that was not to be. The dog ran to within a few feet of Scottie and except for stopping occasionally to tend flea bites behind its ears or on its sides, it kept up with the boy's pace. When Scottie eventually sat on a large rock to rest, the mangy dog crawled

118

up beside him.

"What yah want from me, dog?" The boy reached out and ran his fingers down the dog's bony back. "Yah smell wors'n me. Guess yah got no home and wants to be a hobo dog." He ruffled the stiff hair on the dog's neck. "Well, guess I'll call yah Bo. That's short for hobo." The dog barked and wagged its tail in approval.

****

The vibrating tracks warned of an approaching train long before its headlight could be seen. Scottie ran and snatched the dog by the scruff of the neck as it headed toward the light, dragging it clear of the tracks just as the train rumbled by at such a speed that it sucked wind and threatened to pull them both under the wheels.

"That was a dang stupid thing to do, Bo," he said. "I guess yah need someone to look aftah yah." Letting the dog go, Scottie started jog-

Bo stopped occasionally to scratch his flea bitten hide.

ging for he felt new energy that came with the hope that there was a station somewhere down the line.

Scottie's legs were past aching and his feet were throbbing by the time the stars and moon left the sky and the orange-yellow sun started its climb over the horizon. He knelt beside the tracks when he heard a faint clacking in the distance. Holding his hands on the rails he could feel the vibration of a moving train. "Station ahead," he whispered. "Thank God." Crawling under a clump of low bushes, he fell asleep on the damp ground, oblivious to the persistent mosquitos buzzing around his head.

****

It was afternoon when Scottie turned onto his stomach and

119

looked through the surrounding limbs. Bo was out in the sunshine lying on his back, vigorously twisting his body back and forth giving himself a good scratching. Crawling from his hiding place, Scottie brushed the dirt from his clothes and scratched the bug bites on his face and arms.

"Guess we've both been bit by damn pesky bugs; fleas got yah and skeeters got me." He looked closely at the pitiful dog and shook his head. "In the daylight you're a sorry sight if'n I evah saw one. Just a dirty, bug-bit ugly smelly dog." Bo sauntered toward him. "And don't come near me waggin' your tail like I gave yah a compliment."

Because Scottie's stomach was now rumbling from hunger, he grabbed his bedroll and headed out toward the train station. Climbing onto a large rock, he studied the town. The macadem roads that spread out from the railroad station like spokes of a wheel were lined with impressive rows of houses. Rich people, he surmised, for there were many fancy automobiles parked in the driveways. Hoping that they had servants who would think kindly toward him, he hurriedly headed for the town with Bo at his heels.

In spite of the town's affluent appearance, the people in it were not inclined to have human compassion. The first house Scottie approached had a big wooden sign on the white fence. Must have cost a lot of money to have that sign painted he observed. The magnificent, fancy bold red letters read:

"WE DON'T FEED BUMS OR HOBOES. TRAVEL ON OR BE SHOT."

"Damn poor attitude," Scottie said. "No point in stoppin' at this house. Come on Bo." They went through the town trying one house after another. Any hope for food had turned into total discouragement by the time they reached the outer edge of town. Scottie sat down and held his aching head. He had had doors slammed in his face, been completely ignored by people, and called uncomplimentary names; all of which added up to one big migraine headache.

"Oh, to hell with 'em!" he screamed, angrily running to the last house and jerking the gate off its hinges. Fortunately, no one was around to see him do it. Furiously kicking stones and mumbling to himself, he traveled until his anger was spent.

When he finally looked around, he noticed that the houses were farther apart and the countryside was dotted with small gardens. Patches of yellow and white wild flowers grew in profusion in the fields where milk cows were grazing. Scottie dashed to the first unattended garden he came to and pulled up a handful of carrots and wiped the dirt onto his pants leg. Snapping off chunks of the sweet carrots, he ate while walking. This little bit of food relieved his headache and made him believe that stealing was far easier than begging.

At the next garden he had only picked a handful of green beans when a bullet whizzed past his head. Startled, he dashed up the road out of sight of the house where he stopped and rested while he nibbled on the beans. Bo sniffed at the long green bean offered him, but turned his nose up at it and walked away. The raw vegetables had taken the edge off of Scottie's hunger, but he pushed on hoping he could get a hot cooked meal. He hadn't gone far when Bo began to run back and forth in a dirt driveway, sniffing the ground.

"Yah ain't gonna find no food down there, Bo," Scottie said, "but if you think this house is a good one to stop at, I'll give it a try." He boldly walked up to the small house. Stepping around to the back door he gently knocked. No answer. Desperately, he pounded with his fist on the door casing. His hand stopped in mid-air when the door swung open. A short muscular man with nut brown skin and coal black eyes stared questioningly at him. Bo growled menacingly while the man gestured with his hands and said something Scottie could not understand. Oh, great, Scottie thought, he speaks Spanish or something. I would pick the house of a foreigner. He didn't want to turn away without trying to make this man understand he needed food.

"Quiet, Bo!" Scottie commanded shoving the dog aside with the toe of his shoe. Bo obediently sat and watched.

"Food?" Scottie said while cupping his left hand and raising his right hand back and forth between his mouth and hand. The man's eyebrows tightened into a scowl. Lowering his eyes, Scottie turned his pants pockets inside out and raised his shoulders in a hopeless gesture. The man's eyes lit up as he grinned, showing a row of white teeth that contrasted with his jet black mustache and short beard.

"Oh, comer," the man said, as he rubbed his stomach. Scottie quickly shook his head yes believing that comer meant food. He decided to try to get food for Bo too.

"Comer?" Scottie questioned as he pointed at Bo.

121

"No, No!" the man looked shocked. He shook his head. *"No quiero comer el perro!"*

A dark-skinned woman in the background giggled and the man pointed at Bo and laughed. Scottie stepped back a few feet from the door. Whatever joke this man and woman had between them made him uncomfortable. He turned to leave but the man put his hand on his shoulder and smilingly motioned him to come into the house. When he gestured for him to sit at the table, Scottie gingerly perched on the edge of the chair, with his eyes fixed on the couple.

"Chili," the woman said. A ladle of bean mixture was poured into a bowl and placed on the table in front of Scottie. He stirred it with the wooden spoon she handed him, trying to ignore the acrid smell coming from the mixture. Pieces of red hot peppers and strange undefinable ingredients floated among the watery brown beans.

"Thanks," he mumbled as he nodded in her direction.

"For el perro," she said, stepping to the other side of the table. With a quick motion, a chunk of food was flung across the table. Bo caught it in mid-air, swallowing it whole.

Uncomfortable at being eyeballed by the man and woman, Scottie slowly stirred the chili before taking a mouthful. The hot smell of it made his eyes water. He took a spoonful and swallowed it in a lump. It was like a fireball burning its way to his insides. Never had he eaten anything that strange in his life. It numbed his lips, inside of his mouth and throat.

While he awkwardly picked at the food, the man motioned to the woman and she followed him out the door. Guess they don't know about trusting people alone in their house, Scottie thought as his eyes roamed about the room. The only thing worth stealing was the bowl the chili was in. With his gums and cheeks anesthetized by the chili, he ate a few spoonfuls of the beans before noticing the sugar bowl. He quickly dumped it into the chili, but the sugar just made it taste worse. Scottie was sure this chili concoction would make him sick or kill him. "Here, Bo," he said, shoving the bowl toward the dog.

Bo sniffed at it and with an outraged yip ran out the door with his tail between his legs. Snatching up the bowl, Scottie dumped the chili outside the door and covered it with dirt. The bowl was cleaned by dragging a handful of grass around the inside before he stuck it into his bedroll.

"My insides feel like I could burp flames like a dragon," he complained to Bo as they headed down the dirve. The man and woman looked up and good naturedly waved to him before they returned to weeding the garden. Wish I'd stole their vegetables he told himself. I wanted a hot meal; got one all right; 'bout got my insides singed. Boy! Wish Rod had been here. Scottie laughed a desperate, uncontrollable laugh for right now things were looking ridiculously hopeless.

Scottie heard a brook before he turned the corner in the road. Running to it, he plunged his face into the deep stream. Swishing cold water in his mouth took some of the heat from his innards, but his stomach still felt queasy. Resting on the grass, he listened to the stream cascading over the rocks while Bo lapped at the water.

"Yah needs a bath, Bo." Grabbing the dog by the scruff of the neck, he dragged him struggling and growling into the stream. Holding onto Bo while scrubbing his bristly hair with a sliver of soap was no easy task. He hoped that some of the dirt and fleas were washed away before the dog squirmed loose and defiantly shook himself, showering Scottie from head to toe.

"Hey! Cut that out! Yah oughta be thankin' me. Sprayin' me ain't friendly." Scottie started down the road, leaving Bo to roll in the grass and dirt and then shake himself a few more times before he ran and caught up.

At the edge of town there were several huge pecan trees with outstretched limbs standing guard over a hayfield of newly mowed grass. There was nobody in sight. Crawling over the wall, Scottie darted across the open field. Flattening his thin body against the trunk of a tree, he kept his eyes on the area between him and the house on the hill.

Pecans covered the ground, many still in their heavy pods. It only took Scottie a couple of minutes to fill his pockets with the nuts. Slinking back to the road, he flung his bedroll over his shoulder and started running. He wished he'd noticed that tree earlier; it would have saved him from eating that dang chili stuff.

****

Finding safety behind a screen of tumble weed caught in the stiff tall grass, Scottie cracked and chewed on the sweet nuts. The remaining pecans were stuck into his jacket pocket for safe keeping before he lay down and looked at the clouds. There was a lovely sunset forming. The bright red sun hung low on the horizon with streaks of pink, purple and gold spreading out like rays from it. He wished his mother were here to see it for she loved nature's beauty. Tears streamed down his face as he thought of home.

When fatigue and sadness drained him, he dozed off only to dream that his father was chasing him down the tracks flailing the sewing machine strap as he ran. When a train whistle woke him, he jumped to his feet, relieved to see there was no one there but him and Bo.

"I swear I must be goin' crazy," he said aloud. Grabbing his bedroll, he slung it over his shoulder and watched the string of boxcars like a cat watching a mouse, waiting for the opportunity to pounce.

Scottie at the age of 16 was a lonely but brave young man

The Railroad Bulls Make An Offer

The heat of the day quickly dissipated with the setting of the sun. Night had come, bringing with it storm clouds that blackened the sky. A cold chill hung in the air seeping deep into Scottie's bones. When it began to drizzle, he quickly jammed his knitted hat onto his head and buttoned his jacket under his chin before heading for the cover of the tall grass. Lying on the ground, he pulled the edge of his coat over the dog and hugged it to him so it wouldn't whine or bark. He waited a while before ambling over closer to the train where he stood behind a parked Model A. He had a good, although misty, view at what was going on.

"Looks like a Texas stand-off," he whispered to Bo. On the near side of the train there were ten or so ragged hoboes huddled together staring at three railroad bulls on the opposite side of the couplings. Scottie hardly breathed as he slid under the running board of the Model A and hid in the shadows beneath the car. The police had their guns holstered, but menacingly twirled their billy clubs at their sides. Finally one of the railroad bulls spoke.

"Well, men, whatcha 'fraid of?" His face looked gruesome as the light from his lantern highlighted a twisted smile and dark eyes under bushy eyebrows. He stepped across the coupling and walked around the hoboes. "If we meant yah harm, yo-all would be lyin' face down with a bullet in yah by now." Ambling over to the boxcar nearest the group of men, he rapped its side with his billy club and jerked the door open. "See, there's nothin' in there," he said as he stuck his head inside the darkened boxcar.

The car did look empty, but with night shadows and rain, Scottie couldn't be too sure. He decided to stay under the car a while longer. He thought about the first ride he took on the rails with Rod, Checkas and Whiskas. They had ridden with the brakeman's say so. But that was up North. Now he was in the South. Having the bulls offer a free ride just didn't set right. All those he had come in contact with had whacked him with their billy clubs or shot at him. This unusual, seemingly kind behavior confused him. Desperately anxious to get out of Texas, he finally decided to take a chance. Scooting out from under the Model A, he cautiously approached the group of hoboes.

"Can't trust 'em," he heard one man whisper.

"They's just too eager to get us into that car. Got somethin' up their sleeves," another man said in a low tone. The tapping of rain drops on a newspaper held over one man's head seemed unusually loud as they stood silently wondering what to do.

"Prob'ly get us in and lock the damn door so's we-all die," another added. "No bulls gonna give us a free ride without takin' it out of our hides one way or 'nother. Can't trust these southern good ol' boys."

The three policemen on the other side of the train snickered as they turned and trudged toward the caboose. An useasy cold chill ran through Scottie's body as he thought of the chance he was about to take. He thought it through as best he could. He had outsmarted or out-run bulls on many occasions and he would do it again if trouble started.

"Is it money yah want?" one hobo asked. "I got 'bout three dollar from workin'. Maybe rest of the men could come up with a few more." The policeman silently strolled around the group of hoboes like a prison guard inspecting the inmates. They all eyeballed him, ready to run at the slightest hint of aggression on his part.

"Don't need your money," he replied arrogantly as he poked the hobo in the belly with his billy club. Walking back toward his buddies at the end of the train, the railroad bull muttered, "Think yo-all can buy me for three dollars?"

"Men, we've got to get out of here. It's going to get colder before morning. We're getting soaked now and from the looks of the sky, we're in for a night of it." Scottie turned and looked at a tall impressive man who's calm voice and perfect English was unusual on the rails. "Let's take a chance," the man continued. "But we'll have to use our heads. We'll go to the edge of the yard where the train crosses the road and hop on there. The rain will give us an advantage."

"Okay, we're with yah, Box Car," another spoke up. "But let's git to the train as a group. If bulls shoot, they can't get us all." Box Car was already striding toward the crossing and the men ran to catch up with him.

"When we get inside, a couple of you hold the door open a little so it won't lock. Stay under cover, all of you, in case we get fired upon." The man had a way of taking charge of a situation that demanded respect. Pointing to two men, he added, "*You* and *you* hold the door." There was a grunt of agreement.

As soon as the rods thrust the pistons forward and slowly moved the big wheels, the stack belched black smoke and the whistle sent streams of steam into the air. Whoooooo! Whoooooo! Whoo! Whoooooo! The train slowly approached the curve at the roadway. A frenzied mob leaped toward the empty boxcar. Those in first grabbed the men behind them and yanked them in.

Scottie threw his bedroll and Bo into the boxcar before swinging in. Leaning against the swaying side, he watched the two appointed men quickly slide the door to an almost closed position. They stood straddle-legged as they held it with steady hands while the rest of the group huddled safely behind it. When the train was highballing, someone slipped a spike into the track. The men immediately relaxed their grip on the door. Scottie slid down the rough siding and plunked onto the floor where he sat and strained to look around. It was too dark to make out their features, but he knew where each man was. Bo climbed into his lap and lay there quivering.

"Yeah, I know Bo, noisy old rattler ain't it?" he whispered as he tried to reassure the dog. "It's only the wheels clackin' on the rails." Placing his hand on the dog's trembling body, he said, "Ain't no way yah gonna get outta here 'til the train stops."

A flash of lightning momentarily brightened the interior of the boxcar and Bo looked up with terror in his eyes. An enormous clap of thunder followed causing Bo to shiver uncontrollably. Scottie felt he shouldn't have brought this frightened dog with him. Slowly he stroked the dog's stiff hair as the train lumbered through the hills.

"First time in my years of ridin'," one man stated, 'that I'm travelin' with the bulls' permission. I never'd believed it. Wonder what they're up to anyway?"

"I love the danger of the rails," another man replied. "Makes yah feel alive." No one spoke for a few minutes while jagged streaks of lightning split the sky followed by deafening thunderous booms. The man continued. "I live with danger ev'ry day. This ain't no diff'rent. 'Sides, maybe this time we comes out on top."

"Ye're dreamin'. I'll believe in miracles when we've reached the other end of the line alive." Scottie recognized that raspy voice from somewhere. He squinted into the darkness trying to connect the voice with a face. Their eyes met when another streak of lightning lit up the boxcar. The man's eyes were shiny and glistening like the silver circles surrounding the band on his broad-brimmed hat. Scottie quickly looked away. It was Slick Willy. Although he hadn't seen him in some months, a sickening feeling struck the pit of his stomach at the sight of him. Memories came back of the man stealing a lamb and how it had been killed by smashing its head with a rock.

Fumbling in the darkness, Scottie pulled out his pouch of Bull Durham tobacco and rolled a smoke. Trying to be nonchalant and inconspicuous, he leaned back against the side of the boxcar and dragged on the fag. The chugh-a-chugh of the engine and the clacking of the wheels on the rails made him drowsy as he watched the men through half-closed eyelids.

"Hello boy." The gravelly voice startled Scottie as Slick Willy slid over next to him. "Remember me?"

"Can't rightly say. See a lot of men on the rails."

"I knew a boy back a ways that looked like yah. We got meat for a jungle camp by stealin' a lamb. We smashed its head with a rock. 'Member anythin' like that?"

"Nope. Don't sound like nothin' I evah did." Scottie nervously slid several feet away, dragging his belongings and Bo with him. He hated people crowding him and especially didn't like this man near him. Slick Willy followed, sitting tight by the boy's side.

"I think yah do remember me. Yah lost a bet when you figured I couldn't catch that lamb. Yah owe me somethin' for that."

Scottie remained silent, hoping the man would go away.

"Nice dog yah got," Slick Willy whispered. "Mind if'n I pet him?"

"Don't mind if he don't," Scottie replied, turning his head away from the man's obnoxious breath. A minute later, the boy felt an uneasiness that turned to disgust as he realized the man's hand had slipped inside his pants and was caressing him. Angrily he shoved the hand away and slid further up the wall. Slick Willy continued to follow and pressed against him.

"I always liked your looks boy. Saw you waitin' with the rest for the train. Noticed that man ain't with yah no more," he murmured. "Did he dump yah kid?"

"He went home to his woman in Texas."

"I'll take care of yah now. You owe me a favor. Pay your debt and I'll take care of yah and meet your needs."

"Rod and me had nothin' like that goin'!" Scottie shouted. "I can take care of myself. Get away from me, yah fag!" Slick Willy's arm was like a vice clamping onto Scottie's shoulder and pulling him toward him. He tried to cover the boy's mouth with his other hand. Bo growled as Scottie struggled.

"Leave me alone! Damn you!" Scottie shouted, biting Slick Willy's hand. Doubling his fist, he punched the man in the stomach with all his strength.

"What's happening over there?" Box Car called.

"It ain't nothin'!" Slick Willy yelled. "Nothing to worry about. Just a misunderstandin' between me and the boy."

"It is too somethin'! Man's drunk! Touchin' me all over like I was a girl or a queer!"

"Didn't mean nothin'," Slick Willy said as Box Car grabbed hold of him. "Just pettin' the dog. The boy just misunderstood."

"Liar! You're a fag and I don't want yah near me!"

"Leave the boy alone, or you'll answer to me," Box Car said as he dragged Slick Willy to the far end of the car. "Stay away from him or I'll shove you out the door myself! Damn pervert!" The other men had a good horselaugh over the incident, but Scottie sat and looked with dark hateful eyes toward the blackness where he knew Slick Willy was sitting. He smelled frightened sweat--his own. He felt the man wouldn't take this humiliation without retaliation. He imagined Slick Willy would think no more of slitting his throat than he had the lamb's.

"I'll get yah boy!" Slick Willy called out.

Scottie felt the freedom of riding the boxcars slipping away. Now he realized he was shut in an enclosure with strangers who could take advantage of his vulnerability if he wasn't careful. He rode the rest of the way with his knife in his hand listening for any unusual movements near him.

A Day in the Desert

The train had traveled through the thunderstorm. Off in the distance several stars could be seen through the clouds when the men in the boxcar began to relax. Some of the hoboes sat at the door with legs dangling out, some stood, and others slouched against the car walls letting the rocking of the train put them to sleep. Scottie was still thinking of Slick Willy when the exhausts on the train were cut and sparks flew from the rails.

"Train's slowin'," one man said, standing to pee into the night air. "Seems to be desert 'round here by the looks of the cactus and sand. Stoppin' to take on water, most likely."

By the time the train came to a full stop, three railroad bulls stood at the open door with their guns drawn.

"End of the line, boys. Yo-all had 'nuf free ridin'. Now git out and git walkin'!" one of them commanded.

Scottie bolted for the door with his bedroll over his shoulder and Bo in his arms. He lost his balance as the sand slid under his feet, rolling him down the incline at the side of the rails. Bo, happy to be free from the confinement of the boxcar, squirmed loose from his arms and ran around the cactus plants. He barked in celebration while the disheartened hoboes crowded together and watched the water funnel being lowered to fill the boiler.

"Yah ain't gonna leave us here, are yah?" one man asked the bulls. What a stupid question, Scottie thought. Of course they were going to leave them out here in the desert. His instincts had told him all along that their offer for a ride had been too good to be true.

"Maybe a nice long walk to town will do yah good," one bull remarked. His buddies laughed at their cruel joke.

"But, we'll pay yah." The hobo who had offered money before ran after the railroad bulls. "We offered to give yah money back at the station. Said yah didn't want it then. Will yah take it now? Please." Scottie looked at the hobo in disgust. How could he make such a fool of himself. Didn't he realize there would be no mercy shown here.

"If we wanted anything yo-all got, we'd of taken it by now," one railroad bull growled. "If any of yah try to get back on this train when it starts, yo-all will be buzzard bait!"

"What're we gonna do?" one hobo whispered to his pal.

"Damned if I know," his buddy replied. "Guess we're gonna walk." By the time Scottie scrambled up the incline, the group of men had their bedrolls on their backs, ready to start hiking.

"Wait a minute," Scottie said. "Let's all run for the boxcar soon's they get started. There's only three of them and ten of us. If they get in the empty boxcar, we can overpower 'em. I'm willin' to take a chance. We don't know how far we'll have to walk in this desert 'fore we reach a town."

"Stupid kid. Ain't got a brain in yah head," Slick Willy mumbled.

"Give the kid credit. Sounds like it might work," one man said.

"Soon's they get underway, we'll run as a group," Scottie said convincingly. "We'll outsmart them."

"Okay, we'll give 'er a try," one said. "Beats walkin'."

As the train rolled slowly by them, Scottie dashed toward the boxcar. Looking over his shoulder for the other men, he was terrified to see a railroad bull running behind him and the gap between them closing. The rest of the men were a blur in the background. He could hear Slick Willy's throaty laughter and others calling him to come back, but there was nothing for Scottie to do but keep running. He grabbed the ladder at the back of the last car and climbed to the catwalk. Running its length, he jumped down the ladder at the other end. His knuckles turned white as he held tightly to the brake rod and unsteadily stood on the shifting couplings while the train lumbered along the tracks. Glancing up at the roof, his heart raced when he saw the railroad bull's gun aimed at him. Without thinking, he let go of the brake rod and threw himself out from between the cars onto the sandy desert. With the wind knocked out of him, he lay trembling on the sand, watching the lantern at the back of the train disappear into the distance. It's shrill whistle was frustrating. It was a sound as cruel as Slick Willy's laughter.

"Why didn't yah come along with me?" Scottie asked the hoboes who ran over to see if he was all right.

"'Cause two bulls were standing guard with their guns trained on us while the third one ran yah down. Wished we coulda stopped him or helped yah. We weren't about to tangle with their guns."

"Well, let's stop talkin', and get to it," another said. "You able to hike along with us, boy?"

"Just leave me here," Scottie said wearily. "I'll be okay. Although shook up and wobbly, he didn't want to keep the other men from going their own ways -- especially Slick Willy who was hovering around him.

"I'll be takin' your mutt with me," Slick Willy growled, grabbing the dog up from the ground where he was lying at Scottie's side. "He'll be payment on your bet 'til you gets your strength back."

"He ain't my mutt," Scottie said. "I hope he bites yah!"

Slick Willy stared down at the boy as he tied a rope around Bo's neck. "We'll be in next town waitin' for yah to come." His gravelly voice was low and threatening. "Wants this dog back, come look me up. Yah knows what yah have to do to get it back."

"Don't waste your time waitin'. If I nevah see yah ag'in it'll be fine with me," Scottie said as he turned his back on the man and examined his legs to see if anything was broken. He sadly watched the men gather their belongings and head down the tracks with Bo in tow. He told himself Bo would be all right. He had no real claim on the dog and sure 'nuf would never accommodate Slick Willy even if he never saw the dog again.

The sound of voices slowly faded as the hoboes trudged down the tracks leaving Scottie to face the silence of the desert alone. Lying there in a half conscious state he wondered whether he was imagining movement in the sand near the water tower. He staggered to his feet and squinted into the darkness.

"How are you doing, boy?" The familiar voice of Box Car called to him.

"Doin' just fine," Scottie answered. "I thought everyone had left and I was hearin' a lizard or somethin'."

Box Car chuckled. "No. I'm no lizard. Been called many things, but not a lizard. I just thought I'd use my brain and stay behind. I figure if one train stops for water, another will sooner or later. I don't intend to walk more than I have to."

"I'm surprised the others didn't think about that."

"Think you can make it to the water tower by yourself?" Box Car said, laying his hand on Scottie's shoulder.

"I can!" Scottie indignantly shrugged him away. Although happy the man had stayed behind, his pride wouldn't let him take any help or sympathy. He weaved his way to the water tower where he plunked down, and curled up on the sand. He wished he had the bedroll that had been lost when he jumped from the train, but was too exhausted to go hunting for it. Shivering from the chill of the desert night, he scraped sand over himself to keep his body warm and fell asleep. He didn't notice when Box Car gently laid his jacket over him.

****

A loud snort from Box Car woke Scottie with a start. He panicked as the weight of the sand kept his legs and feet from moving freely. With adrenalin pumping through his body, he flung off the jacket lying on his chest, sprung to his feet, and shook the sand from his clothes. All of the events of the previous night came back as he watched Box Car lying on his back with the brim of his hat pulled down over his eyes. His lips fluttered with each snore, making his long mustache ripple. This was the first good look Scottie had of Box Car and he stood staring at him until another loud snort woke the man. Pushing his hat away from his face, he smiled at Scottie.

"Feel better this morning?"

"Feel just fine." Hesitating for a moment, he said, "By the way, my name is Scottie." Box Car rolled himself onto his feet.

"Well then, Scottie it is." Box Car looked gigantic standing there shielding his eyes from the sun with his hand and peering across the flat desert. "What happened to your bedroll? Lose it on the train?"

"It was 'round my shoulder when I jumped off the train. I think it fell in the sand," Scottie answered.

"Now that daylight is here you should be able to find it, for it wouldn't have fallen far from the track. Why don't you look for it while I heat up some coffee?"

Scottie limped up the track, his eyes searching through the cactus and sage brush. Stumbling along, he finally caught sight of some of his belongings where the wind had scattered them among the cacti. After shaking the sand from his blanket, he made up his bedroll and headed back to the water tower. Box Car had produced a tin pan and was heating coffee over a Sterno can.

"I didn't think yah really had coffee," Scottie said bending over to smell the acrid day-old brew. "Where'd yah get it?"

"Left over from the last jungle. I keep a jar with me and pour part of my cup of coffee into it for later. I have been known to be desperate enough to take the thick grounds from the bottom of a pot and add water to it later," Box Car said jokingly. "A man needs to carry coffee on the rails. It fights the thirst and hunger." Scottie was impressed. That was something he wanted to remember. He had seen coffee poured into the fire many times and wished later he had some of it for his empty stomach.

"It would be nice to have something to eat," Box Car mused as he spit a glob of brown goo onto the sand. "This coffee sure leaves a horrible taste."

"I have somethin'!" Scottie shouted remembering the pecans in his jacket pocket. He quickly shook them onto the sand.

"Well, it wasn't what I was wishing for, but since bacon and eggs seem out of the question," Box Car grinned, "let's get at those pecans." The nuts were devoured as fast as they could be picked out of the cracked shells. Scottie used his hands to sweep sand over the debris.

"Don't want anyone to be searchin' 'round for the culprits what left shells near the tracks."

Box car was studying the tower. "How would you like to get cooled off?"

"Sounds good to me. Want to go swimmin'?"

"I don't think we'll have to," Box Car called from half-way up the ladder. "I'll lower the funnel! We'll take a shower!"

Scottie stripped and watched the water gush out as the funnel was lowered. Box Car jumped down and they ran naked through the water like children through an open fire hydrant. Goose bumps covered Scottie's body as the force of the water massaged his skin. The sand sucked up the moisture like a sponge, until eventually it could hold no more and a puddle began to form.

"I better get that funnel hauled up before a train comes," Box Car said quickly climbing up and fastening the funnel into its original position.

"There," he called. "Let's hope that puddle dries up before a train comes. We wouldn't want to alert the engineer that there's someone around."

Scottie and Box Car hauled their dirty dry clothes onto their sun-dried bodies and retreated to the shade of the tower. Box Car pulled a small book from his pocket and read for a while. Scottie sat silently scrutinizing the desert trying not to disturb him.

"Is Scottie your Christian name?" Box Car finally asked as he put the black book into his shirt pocket.

"I don't think so. I'm too evil to be a Christian."

Box Car laughed at the boy's innocence. "I meant was Scottie the name your Mother gave you?"

Scottie turned his head and stared at the desert, visibly moved by the mention of his mother. After what seemed like a long minute, Box Car said, "Oh well, no matter. Scottie it is."

"Where yah from, Box Car?" Scottie asked, relieved that the man wasn't pressing the subject.

"New England. I used to be a teacher in a one-room schoolhouse until the Depression set in. Then I was given the boot. There was no money to pay me, so the mothers volunteered to teach the children. I've been riding the rails for a while now."

"Don't you have a fam'ly?"

"No. I never got married. There was a girl once. She was a real beauty. The only trouble was that other boys took a liking to her too. A banker turned out to be the lucky guy. They married and had children. I even had a couple of her youngsters in my classroom." Box Car spoke in a dreamy low tone to himself. "Those girls were pretty just like their mother." Then he turned to Scottie and stated, "I just never turned my head for any other woman since. It was God's will that I not marry for I couldn't have taken care of a family while riding the rails."

"I'm sorry things didn't work out for yah."

"That's the way life is, Scottie. You can't take anybody or anything for granted. Circumstances change and people change with them. The Lord God is the only one that doesn't change." Box Car was crawling out from under the water tower as he spoke. "We better find a place to hide before a train comes through." Scottie slid out onto the hot sand and shaded his eyes against the brilliant sun.

"Looks awful flat to me," he said scanning the monotonous brown terrain. "Think any of the cactus big 'nuf to hide behind?"

135

"We'll have to go underground," Box Car observed.

"Whatcha mean? We can't dig no tunnel in sand."

"We can make a trench *under* the tower where we won't be seen."

"Yah got anythin' to dig with?"

"Sure. We have our hands, cups, shoes, or ..." Box Car grinned as he took out his knife, "we can make digging sticks by cutting strips of wood from the tower legs." The morning past as they dug with the sticks and threw the sand away from the trench with their hands. It was slow work but by noon they had a well hidden trench circled by a sloping mound of sand.

"May as well sleep," Box Car said after a stretch of gazing down the tracks. "We probably will be stuck here until night before a train comes through."

While they rested, Scottie noticed a brown snake slithering across the sand toward them. He nudged Box Car and pointed at it.

"Ever eat snake?" Box car whispered to Scottie.

"No, never," he said as he pulled further back into the trench.

Box Car held perfectly still until the snake was almost to the trench. Sensing danger, the snake turned and quickly retreated. In an instant, Box Car had jumped from the trench and was on it. Grabbing it in back of its head, he held it dangling in the air.

"You sure that thing ain't poison?" Scottie said as he scooted further away from the writhing snake. By this time it was wrapping itself around the man's arm.

"It's harmless. I was a school teacher, remember?" Box Car assured him. With his knife, he slashed the snake's head off with a single blow. Its body continued to wriggle while Box Car slit it down the belly and peeled its skin off as easily as peeling a banana. Its innards fell to the sand where Scottie buried them while Box Car chopped the snake into pieces about two inches long. Stabbing a chunk of meat with the sharpened end of his digging stick, he held it over the sterno can until it turned black. After handing the morsel to Scottie, Box Car cooked a piece for himself. They hungrily took turns at sharing the snake meat.

"Good meat," Scottie said as he gnawed the last scrap from the snake's spine. "It's a little squeaky when yah chew it but doesn't taste half bad."

"Sure hope it wasn't poison," Box Car whispered. Throwing his head back, he laughed at Scottie's startled expression. "Too late now," he teased as he settled back into the trench.

****

It was mid-afternoon before the rumble of a train was heard in the distance and the rails began to hum. Scottie and Box Car flattened themselves into the trench waiting for the throttle to be cut and the brakes applied.

"They've stopped," Box Car whispered. "Stay down until they're loaded and ready to leave." Scottie nodded. He wouldn't think of taking any chances because he still felt the bruises that had stranded him here in the first place.

When the train came to a full stop, they watched with bated breath as a man climbed the outside of the tower and lowered the funnel to take on water. Scottie raised his head and viewed the train. It was a short freight composed of five locked boxcars and four flat cars loaded with new tractors. He nudged Box Car and motioned him to take a look. Box Car held his hand flat and slowly lifted three fingers. Scottie knew he was signalling to get on the third flatbed car. He nodded his head in agreement. It was their best chance.

When the boiler was full and the funnel returned to its original position, the railroad men checked the locks on the boxcars and climbed back into the engine. Scottie and Box Car ran and flung themselves onto the flatbed. Rolling between the two rows of tractors, they tightened their grip on the chains that held the machines down.

As they whirled headlong through the desert and into the country-side, Scottie climbed onto a tractor seat. Holding the steering wheel, he made believe he was driving through the fields of wheat and corn. Box Car was on the tractor beside him with the wind blowing his hair around his face and his shirttail flying out behind. They ignored the smoke and cinders gusting around them. Laughing like children with a new toy, they waved at trees, cattle and sage brush like politicians acknowledging their best friends. Rumbling over heavy ground at 60 m.p.h., riding behind that black, fire-eating, smoke-plumed monster, rousing the countryside in its passage, was one of Scottie's happiest journeys.

Photo of a flatbed car taken at Essex Railroad in Connecticut

Working at The Saw Mill

The train whistle at the approach of a rail yard was to hoboes like a shotgun blast to a wild animal. Dropping off the tractors onto the flatbed, Scottie and Box Car bounced with the movement of the train until they could safely jump to the ground. Rolling away from the tracks, they lay flat on their stomachs behind bunches of tall stiff grass and watched while one boxcar was uncoupled and shunted to a side rail. They stayed safely hidden until the short blasts of the whistle signaled and the train clacked on down the tracks.

"I'll go find out where we are," Box Car said pointing toward the small soot-covered station.

"Okay," Scottie whispered.

Raising his head, he watched Box Car disappear into the grime covered building. Streaks of dull yellow paint showed where rivulets of rain had run off the roof and down the siding. Sun shining silver on the tops of the railroad tracks contrasted with the dull layers of dust and cinders around him. He impatiently picked at tufts of grass growing between the rocks on the roadbed as he looked for a likely place for a hobo jungle. There was none. A narrow road wound away from the station and across flat land before disappearing up the mountain and into a forest of trees. A wider road went toward town.

"Didn't mean to frighten you," Box Car said as Scottie scrambled to his feet.

"Just don't like someone so near my back," Scottie said while he vigorously brushed at the dirt on his pants.

"Station master says we're in New Mexico. Don't think we'll find a jungle in this place," Box Car stated. Slinging their bedrolls over their shoulders, they started down the road leading away from the mountain.

139

"Want a drag on my cigarette?" Box Car asked, lighting up one of his hand-rolled fags.

"Sure. Thanks," Scottie said taking a puff and handing it back. Walking in silence, they shared the smoke, all the while keeping their eyes peeled for prospects of food. They hadn't found anything but a patch of wild raspberries when Box Car flipped the butt onto the road and ran over to study a crude carving in a tree trunk.

"Look here!" he whooped. "A sign has been left by a hobo to tell us this farmer lets hoboes sleep in his barn. I reckon he'll be kind enough to give us something to eat besides."

Scottie let out a happy shout at the thought of a place to sleep and food besides. Picking up their pace, they hurriedly passed the barn that sat close by the road. Scottie grinned at Box Car who held his nose as he hustled past a large manure pile in the field.

"You men lookin' to sleep in my barn tonight?" an old man bluntly asked, swinging the door open to Box Car's knock. The pity in the man's eyes made Scottie painfully aware of his long hair and ragged clothes. Shaking his hair away from his face, he carefully slid his dirty hands with their ragged, broken nails into his pants pockets.

"That would be very neighborly of you, sir," Box Car was saying, "but we really are in dire need of food."

"Betsey, give these men the leftovers from suppah." The man motioned to a thin woman fussing around the table who scraped a few pieces of fried chicken and boiled potatoes onto two plates.

"Thank you, sir," Scottie said.

"You are very kind. God bless you," Box Car echoed. They sat on the edge of the porch with their legs dangling and gobbled the food, picking it up with their hands. Scottie and Box Car both turned to face the old man when the door squeaked behind them.

"You lookin' for work?" the man asked. He certainly didn't waste any words Scottie thought.

"Why, yes, we're willing to work," Box Car said. "What kind of work would you like us to help you with?"

"Fussy 'bout what yah do?" the man asked with a crispness in his voice.

"Oh, no," Box Car replied. "It's not that. We just want to make sure it's work we can get at right away. Of course we are willing to work."

"Yeah, we're not afraid of work," Scottie broke in. "Want us to chop wood or somethin' for yah? We can help 'round the farm. Whatevah yah want."

"Oh, it's not for me. It's workin' at the saw mill. They're always lookin' for workers and you both appear to be strong." He stopped and studied Scottie a minute. Then he added, "Boy's a little on the thin side but looks in good shape. You get a dollar a day and a place to sleep and somethin' to eat." The old man pointed a bony arthritic finger toward the purple mountain in the distance. "The camp's up there."

"And how far is it to this saw mill?" Box Car asked.

"Too far to walk. Sleep in my loft tonight and I'll take yah to camp in the mornin'. It's my brother who's the boss there. He's always lookin' for extra help."

"Sounds good to me," Box Car said while pumping the man's hand.

"Thank you, Mr.," Scottie said as he turned and headed for the barn.

****

The cows in their stanchions nuzzled Scottie and Box Car as they walked down the narrow aisle that led to the ladder of the hay mow.

"Wish these cows would stop slobbering on me," Box Car complained as he shoved on the forehead of an exceptionally aggressive cow with saliva hanging like a string from her mouth. Scottie affectionately scratched and patted their heads and necks.

"They're just sayin' hello," Scottie said. "They likes yah."

"I never cared for cows!" Box Car retorted, flattening himself against the wall and hurrying past their outstretched necks. Scottie felt superior to Box Car at that moment when he saw the grown man afraid of a cow. The makeshift wooden ladder leading up to the hay mow groaned under their weight. Scottie intentionally flung his bedroll high over the hay, startling the chickens roosting on the rafters. He laughed as Box Car shielded his head with his arms and dodged the flying, flapping, noisy birds. Not until the hens calmed down and hopped back to their roost did Box Car dare to spread his bedroll in the corner and bed down.

Scottie couldn't sleep right away. The smell of cow manure and musty hay brought back good memories of the team of horses he drove while working on Johnson's farm back home in Rhode Island when he was fourteen. He remembered how grown up he had felt being in command of those large animals pulling the hay wagon. The cutting and pitching hay in the summer heat had been tiresome but Mrs. Johnson's cold lemonade and home baked cookies in mid-morning made it worth the while. He was still picturing those horses with their glistening chestnut colored backs when he fell asleep. Unfortunately he could not control his mind while asleep. His recurring nightmare tormented him. Once again he saw an image of his father with a switch in his hand chasing him down the railroad tracks. When morning noises roused him, he sat bolt upright with sweat pouring down his face. It was barely daylight. Peering down over the edge of the hay mow he watched a rooster strutting around the cows' feet preening and crowing like he owned the place. Hens were peacefully pecking at debris on the barn floor.

The animals had a calming effect on the boy. Safe in the hay mow he listened to the clanging of milk pails as the farmer meandered in and walked from cow to cow, talking to each one by name.

"I'll help yah with the milkin'!" Scottie called.

"Evah done it before?" The man looked up doubtfully.

"Many times. I worked on a farm when I was only twelve."

"Well, here's a bucket. Come on down. Start with Daisy here."

Hustling down the ladder, Scottie seated himself on an upside down milk crate beside the brown and white Guernsey. When he pressed his head against her flank, she turned and curiously eyeballed him before returning to the grain trough. After getting the milk flowing, Scottie turned the cow's teat toward his mouth and squirted warm milk down his throat while he pushed several cats aside with his feet. When Box Car noticed what Scottie was doing, he came down the ladder and waited until the farmer wasn't looking. Then he tossed his cup on the hay by Scottie's feet. Although he wouldn't get near the cows, Box Car kept his eyes on the cup between Scottie's knees and when it was filled and slid toward him, he joyfully chugged it down.

"Daisy seems to be short of her usual milkin'," the farmer said as he hefted the bucket. "Yah sure yah milked before?"

"Yes, sir! I'm sure!"

Scottie and Box Car watched the farmer try to strip more milk from Daisy. Picking up the crate, Scottie winked at Box Car before going

142

to the next cow. Although the milk would have tasted better cold, it was like a balm to the empty stomachs of the hungry hoboes.

When the milking was finished and the cows herded out to pasture, Scottie and Box Car waited by the side of the road while the farmer cranked up his Model T truck.

"Hop in!" he called. Leaning out the window, he handed Box Car a bunch of fried potatoes wrapped in newspaper. "Here's breakfast for you and the boy," he said.

Box Car crawled over the tail gate while Scottie jumped from the fender into the bed of the truck. The potatoes were gobbled as they bounced along past the train station and up the rough winding road . It followed a river filled with large Ponderosa pine logs floating downstream. Halfway up the mountain the crashing of trees as they hit the ground, a gas engine laboring to push a saw, and men yelling back and forth could be heard.

Nearing the camp, Scottie watched in amazement as huge logs were lifted onto skids and then rolled onto the carriage to be clamped down. There was activity and noise everywhere.

"Brought yah a couple of hands," the farmer told his brother. "They look strong and willin' to work hard, Stumpy. Told them yah might put them to work." Stumpy walked over to them quickly in spite of the fact he had one wooden leg. He sized up Scottie and Box Car.

"Yeah, I can use yah. Guess my brother told yah what the deal is. You sleep over there." He pointed to a made over chicken coop. "You'll get two meals and $1.00 a day, enough to keep you in smokes and still save a little, or spend on booze if you're so inclined." The sleeping quarters didn't look too great but Scottie was grateful for the work -- with pay.

"*You*," Stumpy said pointing to Box Car, "Give your name to the paymaster and then start work with Howie over there loading logs from the skid to the carriage. He'll show yah how to clamp them so's they won't roll off."

"Thank you, sir," Box Car said tossing his bedroll against the base of a tree and heading toward Howie for instructions.

"You, boy, can carry slabs up the grade. Pile them where the others are puttin' them." Scottie watched a man with a slab on his shoulder, walking up the grade. It looked like heavy work but Scottie was willing to give it a try.

143

After eating supper of a mixture that passed for stew, Scottie and Box Car found their sleeping quarters. As they lay on their cots, Scottie stared at the holes in the rotted ceiling while Box Car read from his little book.

"Can you read, Scottie?" Box Car asked.

"Sure. Had four years of schoolin'. Of course I can read."

"I didn't mean to offend you. I thought you might like to have this book to read in your spare minutes." He held out the black book.

"Nah, I couldn't take that. You like to read it a lot."

"Well, I can get another one. Besides I have a lot of it memorized and stored inside my head." Box Car held it closer to Scottie. The letters on the cover had once been embossed in gold but now were worn and hardly legible.

"Thank you. A New Testament," Scottie said as he took the book. "I never had a Bible before. I have been to church once or twice but never had a Bible or a book of any sort that was all my own." Scottie felt honored that Box Car had given him his book and blinked his eyes several times to keep the tears away. He flipped through the pages and read here and there, but his eyes were tired and none of it made sense to him. Finally he put it in his pocket, turned on his side, and went to sleep.

After two weeks of hard work, sore muscles, and watered-down stew twice a day, Scottie was getting sick of the saw mill. Every time a train whistle blew down in the valley, his desire to leave the camp grew greater. Longing to be back on the rails, but not wanting to hike all the way down the mountain, he planned to stay until he could hitch a ride with the farmer when he came to see his brother.

It was almost two weeks later on a Friday night, right after payday, that Scottie heard the Model T straining its way up the grade. Gathering his belongings, he sat under a tree by the mill and watched while the brothers visited. When the old farmer headed for the Model T, Scottie ran over to him.

"Want help startin' the truck?" he eagerly asked.

"Why, thank yah boy. Give her a yank." Scottie gave the crank a couple of hefty jerks that started the engine right away. He stood back until the truck started moving , then he quickly jumped into the truck bed and lay flat under the window of the cab where he felt the farmer couldn't see him in his rear view mirror. When they got to the railroad station, the Model T stopped.

"Hop on out, boy!" the farmer called.

"Thought you didn't know I was hitching a ride," Scottie laughed.

"I don't miss much," the farmer hollered. "God go with you!" He grinned and waved. Scottie turned and waved again before diving into the tall grass behind the railroad station. Watching carefully to make sure no one was around, he took out his money and counted it. He had twenty-one dollars saved. Taking the money, he made sure there was only one or two dollars in each hiding place. He slid some in the lining of his jacket and the rest in his pockets, bedroll and socks. He had learned that hoboes weren't above beating up or killing another person, including another hobo, for the chance to get themselves a bottle of booze or cigarette makings. This money was intended for his Mother and he determined that he would guard it with his life.

Slick Willy

Scottie knew a train came through every night about dusk for he had timed the whistles while working at the sawmill. When the sky was turning pink and the sun was about to disappear below the horizon, he arrived at the station and positioned himself behind clumps of grass where he could watch for another hobo. He hadn't located any when the whistle signaled for the approaching train. Scanning the freight as it slowly came to a stop, he noticed that one boxcar was unlocked. Keeping low to the ground, he crawled behind the tall grasses and brush. Like a lioness stalking its prey he moved slowly until he was opposite the chosen car. He stayed with his muscles taut until the familiar whoo! whoo! signaled that the train was ready to move out. Then he raced into action.

Getting into a boxcar was easy for him now. In a matter of seconds he was standing in the dark interior with his body plastered against the wall. Peering around inside the car, he was convinced he was alone. Although not sure which direction the train was going as it highballed over the tracks, he could tell it was climbing into the mountains. Even his jacket buttoned around his neck and his hat pulled over his ears was little protection from the cold howling wind that swirled dust and bits of paper around him.

Holding tightly to the door frame, he reached outside for a railroad spike. There was none. Knowing he had to jam something into the track in order to shut the door part way, he rifled through his belongings. All he could find that might work was his knife which fit tightly into the track with the tip of the blade stuck into the wooden door frame. This kept the door open about six inches to let in air. Now that the wind had been subdued, he wrapped up in his blanket. He was so fatigued from working all day that he slept soundly and did not hear when the whistle

146

sounded for the next station.

The crashing of the boxcar jolted Scottie awake. He was tossed up and then dropped with a thump that made his back slam into the side wall. Startled, he struggled to his feet. The car collided again, flinging him onto the floor. Panic-stricken with uncertainty at what was going on inside the dim interior of the boxcar, he hysterically felt for the door and tried to pull it open. It was tightly shut and locked. He pounded on the door until his hands were bruised and yelled for help until his throat was sore, but there was only silence outside.

Sitting on the floor, he breathed slowly to calm his fears and try to figure out how to get out of there. A thin stream of light shining through a crack gave him hope. Rushing to it, he plastered his eye tightly against the wall. All he could see was tall grass growing by the tracks. There was no sound of an engine puffing, no rumbling on the tracks; only a scary stillness. He knew now he was locked in a boxcar that had been shunted to a siding. The loud crashes that woke him had to be from the impact of the cars humping.

Not knowing what else to do, he felt around on the floor for his knife. His fingers trembled as they touched the hard metal handle. How the knife got free from the track he could only imagine. It could have jiggled loose while the train rumbled over the rails or popped out when the cars collided. The alternative thought that frightened him was that some railroad bull had pulled the knife free and thrown it into the car before locking the door knowing, someone was inside. He felt stupid and panicky again. Perhaps it would be days before anyone would come to get the cars, especially if they had been shunted somewhere along the line between stations. He crawled to the gleam of light again and furiously dug around the hole with his knife. Slivers of wood fell to the floor, but a metal shell on the outside of the car kept him from breaking through. He sat and held his head in his hands. Tears splashed to the floor as he thought of his Mother and family. He was sure he would never see them again. This boxcar would be his coffin.

When the sun set, Scottie was left shivering inside the cold, dark boxcar. He lit a fire from paper and litter he found around the floor and piled the slivers of wood on top. Rolling a cigarette, he smoked while he watched the comforting flame of fire. The car was slowly filling with smoke. All throughout the scary night he slept fitfully from the lack of oxygen.

147

It was dawn when the disoriented boy heard heavy footsteps outside moving along the creaking boards. The sound of someone fiddling with the lock on the door aroused him enough so that he went over to the door and kicked it with his shoe. His yell for "help!" only sounded like a whisper inside his head. When he heard the clicking of the lock, feeling certain a railroad bull was waiting for him, he prepared to jump. When the door slid open, a brakeman was surprised to see Scottie appear from the center of a billow of smoke that puffed out the door.

"Whatcha doin' in there?!" the brakeman hollered as he waved the smoke away from his face and looked inside. "You almost burned a hole through the floor. Could've set the car on fire and died in there." The brakeman turned and walked away. "Foolish youth," he mumbled.

"Do yah know where there's a hobo jungle 'round here?" Scottie called after the man. He felt he was pushing his luck, but figured the man would have harmed him by now if he was going to. The man kept walking.

"Not familiar with them, but if I was you, I'd look down by the creek that runs beside the track," he hollered over his shoulder. "In that direction."

Scottie hurried up the tracks in the direction the man had pointed until he reached a hobo jungle. Several men sat around talking and drinking coffee. A short thin man noticed Scottie standing at the edge of the clearing and waved him over to where he was sitting.

"They call me Lefty," the man said as he held out a few crackers to Scottie. "Yah look like yah could stand some crackers and coffee. It ain't much but we'll be gettin' somethin' together by noon."

"Thank yah. I sure could stand somethin' to eat," Scottie said as he got himself some coffee and sat down next to Lefty. "Ain't had food for a while."

As Scottie looked at the men on the other side of the jungle, his heart began to race. There was Slick Willy sitting studying the ground with Bo beside him. Scottie quickly looked away. A few minutes later he had the feeling someone was staring at him. He glanced over toward Slick Willy and their eyes met. Slick grinned and pointed at Bo as he gestured for Scottie to come over to where he sat, but the boy ignored him. If he thinks I'm going after Bo and get near to him again, that man has another think coming. From then on, Slick Willy made Scottie

Scottie's heart raced as he looked across the clearing and saw
Slick Willy with Bo sitting beside him.

149

uncomfortable by watching him, while Scottie kept alert and tried to figure out a way to leave this jungle unnoticed as soon as he could.

"What's that pickup truck drivin' long side us for?" Scottie asked Lefty. "Is he a railroad bull?"

"Nah," the man chuckled. "He's lookin' for someone what wants to earn three dollars in a hurry."

"What's he want them to do?"

"Just get into the truck. The man drives them down to a clump of trees and they walk into the woods. They comes out later, about 10 to 15 minutes. That's all."

"Is he a fag?" Scottie asked scornfully.

"You might say that," Lefty chortled.

"See that man?" Lefty said as he nudged Scottie. They watched Slick Willy sauntering over to the side of the road. The truck stopped and Slick talked to the driver for a minute before he lifted Bo into the back of the truck . Then he climbed into the cab. He's taking Bo so I won't be able to get him back Scottie thought. Well, if he wants the dog, he can have him. If he figures I owe him somethin', he can have the dog. Ain't my dog anyway. He ain't gonna get me to be his lover.

Just as Lefty had said, the men went into the woods down the road a ways and when Slick Willy returned the man handed him a piece of paper before he drove off.

"Yah noticed that guy that went in the truck didn't yah?"

"Yeah, I saw 'im," Scottie answered.

"Him and that dog been hangin' 'round the jungle for a week or more according to what I hear. Said he's waitin' for someone. And been collectin' himself a few bucks in the meantime."

"Didn't look like he got money to me," Scottie said. "It must have been a check or an I.O.U."

"You are observant," Lefty laughed. "You're right. The man would be a fool to come ridin' 'round a jungle with money in his pockets."

Scottie hardly heard what Lefty was saying for his mind was on the fact that Slick Willy was constantly staring at him and several times had tried to get close to him. Knowing Slick Willy wouldn't try anything with all the other men around, Scottie spent the morning making sure he wouldn't get himself caught in a compromising position . When the group spread out into the town to get stuff for a gumbo, Scottie made sure he had Lefty and his pal Tatters near him.

It was the middle of the afternoon when the pickup truck was back with a different man driving it. Scottie pointed it out to Lefty.

"There he goes now, headed for the truck again."

As soon as Slick Willy and the truck had driven away, Scottie took the opportunity to hurry to the rails on the other side of town. He was disappointed to find the train heading out had only cattle cars and locked boxcars. The railroad bulls were nowhere in sight for they didn't look for hoboes in open cattle cars. There was too much danger involved when hoboes rode with the crowded animals, some of them still with long horns and nasty dispositions.

Scottie believed this cattle car full of bawling animals was his way out of town. Seeing the side door left open to give the animals air, reinforced that idea. Strolling the length of the car, he peeked through the slats. He felt he could make it safely to the empty hay storage area at the front of the car. A narrow corridor made between a barrier and the side of the car would be his route.

The top and two ends of the cattle cars were solid to keep the wind and rain from the animals while the sides were open to give them air. Horizontal slats were evenly placed up the sides to keep the cattle in. A movable barrier inside separated the cattle from the hay storage area. Hoboes would usually cling to the slats as high above the cattle as they could and work their way down to the storage area in order to ride inside a cattle car. Because there were no railroad bulls around, Scottie swung himself through the door and crawled on his stomach down the narrow alley. The heat and stench made him feel like retching. Once he was safe in the storage area, he stuck his nose out through the slats and breathed deeply until his head cleared and his stomach settled.

The cattle stopped bawling and shoving on the barrier as the train clacked over the rails. Scottie bunched up a little hay left on the floor and made himself a seat in the corner. From there he kept his eyes on the cattle and stayed tensely alert, ready to climb up the slats of the car if he needed to.

When the whistle blew and the brakes were applied, the cattle again became aggressive. Scottie climbed the side slats above their heads and worked his way to the door, where he dropped down, sprung to the ground and ran up the tracks before the train came to a full stop.

Tennessee Coal Hopper

Hard Tack had joined Scottie after they jungled up together at a little camp in South Carolina. Scottie had liked him from the start although the man looked like he had just crawled out of a coal mine. He was black from head to foot with dirt and soot. Only white eyeballs and large white teeth could be seen as he grinned. The visor on his cap was half gone and tattered at the edge where he had chopped it off with a knife.

As they walked side by side toward a train, goose bumps covered Scottie's arms. This happened whenever he saw one of the powerful black monsters standing on the tracks, gently wheezing and coughing out steam and smoke. Dirt, grime and cinders falling from the clouds of steam didn't deter his enthusiasm as he and Hard Tack hustled toward the rail yard.

"What a long train!" Scottie exclaimed as he repositioned the bedroll on his back and balanced himself on the rail, mimicking a tight-rope walker.

"Doesn't look promising," Hard Tack replied. His comment went unheard. Scottie was studying the train and scanning the yard for the railroad bulls.

"Hear me?"

"Nope. Sorry."

"Get yahself together. We've got to ride out of here and that train has no empty boxcars. They's all locked. Quit yah clownin' 'fore the bulls notice us."

"Never seen so many coal cars before," Scottie remarked as he continued to look for an empty boxcar. They darted from car to car, to piles of railroad ties, like soldiers behind enemy lines.

"Got to be someplace to ride," Scottie said optimistically.

152

"We cain't ride the catwalks. There's still too much daylight."

"We'll find a place." Scottie pointed. "How 'bout the fourth car back?"

"Yo-all crazy! That's a coal car."

"When it's loaded, we'll climb under the end of the hopper."

"Nah! We can't both fit in that little space up front of the hopper. The bulls would see us for sure. What's the mattah with yah head?"

"We'll fit," Scottie replied as Hard Tack doubtfully shook his head.

"Nah! Yo-all crazy!"

The hopper on the coal car was shaped like the top of a large "V", leaving a small triangular open space under the slanted steel. One man could lay across the underbracings and hang onto the uprights and ride safely. The two of them would have to lie side by side, causing one to be squeezed into the narrow wedge and the other to be dangerously close to the outer edge.

They settled themselves behind a screen of brush and limbs to watch the train while Scottie had a smoke.

"How come yah don't smoke nor chew?" Scottie asked, snuffing out his cigarette.

"My old lady don't like it. Quit before I started ridin' the rails. Couldn't afford it no how." He grinned as he lay on his back and stared at the sky. "'Sides, I just got too much pride to pick up stubs outta the dirt and save the tobacco till I get enough to roll a fag. Glad I gave it up. If yah had been smart yo-all would nevah started up."

Scottie almost retaliated by reminding Hard Tack of the man's lack of a bath and the filth he was carrying around on his body, but decided he was better off keeping quiet. After a stretch of silence, he asked Hard Tack, "What made yah leave home?"

"A woman. That's what puts most tramps on the road. She just couldn't stand my not takin' a bath. But I'm gonna go back home to see the old gal soon," he said as he winked and grinned. "Yah missin' your folk?"

"Not much," Scottie answered. "Just miss my Ma. My old man can go to hell for all I care."

"It takes a lot of tryin' to get 'long with a fam'ly, God knows, but it might be worth yo-all givin' it a try ..."

"Maybe. Some day," Scottie rudely interrupted. Settling back in silence, he kept his eyes on the rail yard.

"Cops comin'," Hard Tack whispered. Sliding onto their bellies into the deeper underbrush, they watched as the men passed within twelve feet of them, looking under the cars and parting the bushes with their billy clubs. Scottie held his breath and hoped he was well camouflaged. After completing their inspection, one cop stood on the platform smoking a cigarette while the other kept an eye on the yard.

The brakemen hurried from car to car checking the couplings and air hoses. Occasionally, one pulled out his pocket watch and noted the time. When he backed up a few steps and studied his timepiece, Hard Tack nudged Scottie's ribs.

"Soon's the brakeman gives the engineer the signal, yah crawl into the end of the hopper. I'll be right behind yah, so don't waste time."

"It's done," Scottie replied enthusiastically.

The engineer was ready to start his run when steam hissed and the brakes were released. The stack blew clouds of black smoke into the air in angry puffs and the rods pushed the big wheels forward.

Scottie kept low as he approached the coal car. Putting his foot on the bottom of the metal ladder, he grabbed the first wrung and swung himself into the open space. Quickly sliding into the narrow opening he looked back. Hard Tack was standing in the bushes grinning. Scottie gave him a feeble wave when he realized that the man had no intention of coming with him. Guess he knew there wasn't much room in here. Maybe he'll jump on a car further back. Holding tightly to the bottom of an upright, Scottie forced his body as far back against the hard metal as he could. His heart raced with the excitement and thrill of another ride on a powerful train.

The ride on the hopper was much more uncomfortable and cramped than Scottie had imagined. He was jerked up and down on the bracings. Pieces of coal bounced back and hit him and coal dust blackened his body as the train clacked over the section of rails.

"What the hell," Scottie muttered when the train stopped at a small station. Scrunching tighter against the hopper, he watched two black men leap up the ladder to the top of the coal car. Coal came raining down like hailstones hitting the ground. He strained to see what he could while keeping himself out of sight. There were about ten black children of various sizes and ages picking up coal and putting it into sacks. "Well, I nevah. Them niggers gettin' themselves some free coal," Scottie murmured. He watched with amusement as the fuzz chased the children from one side of the car to the other, only to see them scoot under the train and come up on the other side of the rails where they grabbed more coal before running again.

"Get down from there!" one cop yelled as another hail of coal rained onto the ground. "You no-good thieves!" the other screeched. With angry threats, the cops climbed the ladder, their billy clubs whacking menacingly against the ladder rungs. Scottie lay still and held his breath. He was thankful the cops had their eyes on the men on the top of the coal car and didn't notice him.

"Damn you niggers! Get off this train! Damn robbers!" The cop's voices were angry and filled with hatred, reminding Scottie of his father when he was drunk. His heart thumped as he heard the yelling from the black men and the sliding and rolling around that caused showers of coal to fall to the ground like a black waterfall.

"Yah lazy good for nothin' thieves!" one shouted again. A scream of pain pierced the air and then another screech. Soon the fracas and shouting stopped and the beaten bloodied bodies of the two black men fell to the ground where they lay unconscious. The frightened children

Riding on the front of a coal car under the hopper was more
uncomfortable than Scottie had imagined.

155

ran to the bushes and stared out with wide startled eyes while a cop poked at the men with his billy stick. One man groaned when rolled over by the policeman's shoe.

When the train began to roll, Scottie looked back at the ragged children standing by the men's bodies. These black men had taken a great risk to get coal for their families. Scottie was grateful this ruckus had saved his hide from a beating, but the circumstances stayed in his mind and he found himself praying that the brave men had not been killed.

Photo of brakeman riding ahead of a coal hopper.

Old Muzzurree

The day had started with a hobo's worst nightmare. When Scottie and three other men arrived at a yard just before sunrise, their timing had been off. They stayed on the train longer than they should have. Before they realized what was happening, a railroad bull swung himself with one hand into the boxcar. A lantern lit every corner as the large man stood in the doorway, blocking their escape.

"You're all dead men!" he bellowed with a yell that sent shivers up Scottie's spine. Sliding his billy stick from his belt, the cop whacked the hoboes backs and jabbed their stomachs, herding them toward the open door. When Scottie tried to sneak past him, a swift kick with the man's heavy shoe sent him hurling out the door and onto the hard cinders that crunched like glass. The rest of the men were knocked about and beaten until they jumped to avoid being killed.

"Don't let me catch yah on this line again, you sonsobitches!" the rough voice screamed into the darkness. A warning shot motivated them to run for cover.

"I'm headin' back to the rail yard," one man said after they had put about a mile's distance between them and the trains. "I'd rathah take my chances with the bulls than travel down a road that prob'ly doesn't lead no where. My feet are achin' already."

"I'll go with yah," another man said. "How 'bout you two?"

"Nah," Scottie stated. "I'm goin' to find a town and visit Sally's so's I can get cleaned up."

"I'll stay with the boy," replied an older man who Scottie guessed was about sixty years old.

Scottie jogged ahead at a rapid pace. There wasn't a spot on his body that wasn't itching, bruised or just plain hurting. Traveling fast helped him forget his misery and he didn't take kindly to having an old

157

man tagging along. He dug at the lice in his thick hair as he hurried to get away and find a place to rest before the inevitable heat of the sun would slow him down.

"Hey, wait for me!" he heard the man call. Slowing a bit, he let him limp along behind him until he caught up.

"I'm from Muzzurree. You'n me goin' the same way. Let's team up 'til we get to town. Whatcha say?" Scottie made no reply but walked a little slower for the man's sake.

"What happened to yah leg, Muzzurree?" Scottie asked. "Why yah limpin' so bad?"

"Hurt myself jumpin' off the train."

"Oh," Scottie replied. Pride was one thing that men didn't lose while riding the rails. They would help one another if asked, but a man would be insulted if offered help, so they traveled in silent misery.

Approaching the edge of a town, the sun warmed their backs while they searched for wild berries, fruit trees, and edible weeds in the pastures and along the stone walls. Muzzurree grinned as he hobbled over to a fence post where he pointed to a sign carved into the wood.

"Here's a sign left by a hobo. We can get somethin' to eat at this place," he said. When they started up the dirt drive, two big German Shepherd dogs stopped them in their tracks. The dogs growled and sniffed them while Scottie talked softly to them.

"Don't mind the dogs! They won't bite!" a middle-aged woman called from the garden. Scottie and Muzzurree hesitantly walked to the garden with the black guardians barking and growling beside them. As they approached the woman, she called to the dogs to shut up. Straightening up, she squinted at the two strangers while vigorously shaking the dirt from a bunch of carrots. Her face, tanned and dried from hours in the sun, was liver-colored. Scottie's insides tightened with the memory of the gardens his mother had planted every year and how hard she worked in them only to have his Pa sell them or move to another house before she could harvest the fruits of her labors. Picturing his mother on her hands and knees coaxing the plants to grow almost brought him to tears.

"Me and the boy here are travelin' through, headin' for town. Would yah like help in the garden for givin' us a little somethin' to eat?" Muzzurree was saying. "We'd gladly help yah pull carrots, M'am. Woman like yo-all shouldn't be gettin' those hands all dirty. We'd gladly help yah."

"The carrots go in that." She pointed to a bushel basket setting about halfway up the row. Hefting a basket full of green beans, she headed for the house with the two dogs by her side. "Fill it up, and don't go stealin' anythin' and I'll give yah both a bite to eat!" she hollered back to them.

"Man, she sure has a large garden," Scottie observed. "She must be cannin' all night."

"Maybe she sells the veg'tables to a market," Muzzurree said as he started pulling carrots. After wiping the dirt onto his clothes, he smacked loudly as he ate the sweet stubby orange carrots before starting work. "Gotta have energy latah on," Muzzurree said, slyly putting a bunch of carrots into his pocket.

They were still in the same long row of carrots when their basket was filled and the woman appeared with sandwiches and milk.

"Sit on the stone wall and eat," she stated bluntly before getting down to the job of picking more beans.

"Thank yah, M'am. God bless yah. Thank yah, M'am, God bless yah," Muzzurree repeated as they withdrew to the wall. He waved to her as she looked up. "God bless yah real good for your kindness, M'am."

"Will yah shut up and eat," Scottie said as he bit into the homemade bread slathered with butter. "Muzzurree, yah 'bout made me puke. Why yah grovel and thank the woman so much?"

"She's kind. She deserves a place in heaven if anyone does."

"Oh, eat yah sandwich and keep quiet!" Scottie snapped. The man sure was irritating him. Quickly gulping his milk, he jumped from the wall and hustled down the drive, running from the thoughts and emotions tearing at his insides.

"Hey, wait for me!" Muzzurree called.

"Catch up if yah can," Scottie said. "I'm travelin' on." A few minutes later, he glanced back. Muzzurree was staggering toward him with his hand on his hip, trying to run to catch up. His face was twisted in pain.

"Oh, hell," Scottie said. He stood and waited.

****

It was almost noon before Scottie and Muzzurree saw the outlines of large buildings.

"I do believe we're comin' into a town," Scottie said. "I sure hope they have a Sally's." The only times he visited the Salvation Army was when he needed to get cleaned up or wanted a new set of clothes. This was definitely one of those times. They continued walking in silence, each with his separate pain and private thoughts.It was Muzzurree who broke the silence,

"Hear that stream comin' up?"

"Yeah. I hear it."

"We can get a drink. Maybe rest a while?"

"Maybe."

The stream was in a beautiful little park. Huge roots of the large trees along the banks spread across the ground. Like elephant trunks they extended into the edge of the water for a drink. Flowers bloomed among the rock gardens. The grass was lush and neatly trimmed. A woman, pushing a baby carriage with a toddler at her side, hurried away toward the other side of the park. Two old men sitting under a tree stared at them and sadly shook their heads.

Scottie ran and stuck his face into the water, drinking like an animal. Wetting his head he scrubbed his scalp in an effort to get rid of some of the lice. He would have liked to strip and jump into the water, but knew with the people watching, he might get arrested. He did venture to take off his shoes and let his blistered feet dangle in the water while he lay back on the soft grass, smoked, and rested.

Visiting Sally's

The sun was high in the sky when the two wanderers drifted toward the outskirts of Chattanooga, Tennessee.

"Sally has a house right near the tracks," Muzzurree said with a smirk, glancing sideways at Scottie.

"Yah knowed it all the time!" Scottie shouted. "How come yah didn't tell me?"

"Thought I'd s'prise yah. It's right by the railroad tracks. I been there before."

"Yah shoulda opened yah mouth and told me."

"Why?"

"Just shoulda. That's all," Scottie said angrily, giving his feelings over to an irritation that had built up since the man joined him.

"Well, mission's right 'round the corner," Muzzurree crisply replied. "Down that next street to the left."

Scottie raced down the sidewalk away from the man. The smell of smoke in the air, the sound of hissing steam and blackened buildings assured Scottie that he was indeed heading for the trains. The Salvation Army building at the edge of the rail yard was an old run-down house with a sway-backed roof. Although covered with smoke and cinders, it sure looked good to the scuzzy, famished boy. A large hand-written cardboard sign hung askew, clinging to the side of the building with the help of one nail in the corner. It read:

MEETING TONIGHT AT 6:00 P.M.
FREE SUPPER FOLLOWING
ALL WELCOME
Bed for the night 25¢

Scottie slipped into the sun drenched room, awkwardly aware of his uncombed, unwashed appearance. He hung his head as a young clean shaven man, handsomely dressed in a dark blue suit, headed toward him.

"I'm Parson Troy," he said, smiling and extending his hand.

"I'd shake yah hand, but wouldn't want to get dirt on yah," Scottie mumbled, feeling the blood rush to his face.

"Doesn't matter to me *or the Lord*," the Parson replied. Tightly grabbing Scottie's hand, he pumped it up and down while studying the boy's face. "If you would like to clean up, there's a shower in the back room. The water might be cool, but you're welcome." To a boy used to bathing in cold streams and ponds, the idea of having luke warm water was more than he had hoped for.

"Mind if my buddy comes along too?"

"Of course not. He's welcome to share what we have."

Scottie motioned to Muzzurree who had slunk in and was sitting inconspicuously on a bench toward the back of the room. The man quickly jumped up and limped along behind Scottie and the Parson to a back room.

"Perhaps you would like a haircut," the Parson suggested, directing his remark to Scottie. "Slim here does a real good job."

"I ain't a real barber, but I can cut hair so's it looks decent and makes a man feel better," the tall thin man said cheerfully as his scissors snipped at the air.

"Well, thank you, sir," Scottie said, sitting in the chair in front of the man. "Sure 'preciate it." Scottie's thick hair was soon falling to the linoleum like strands of seaweed washed onto beach sand. Muzzurree wanted nothing to do with Slim and his scissors. He wanted to keep the fringe of white hair that hung like a frame around his balding head. As soon as the Parson handed him a towel and a small bar of soap, Muzzurree stripped and escaped into the shower stall.

"Yah better throw those clothes yah were wearin' in that barrel over yondah", Slim said when Muzzurree stepped out a few minutes later, dripping wet with the towel wrapped around his waist. "Pick out a clean outfit from the piles over there." Slim pointed to a mound of clothes on the floor. "I'll be back shortly if yah need any help findin' your size."

When Slim closed the door, Scottie furtively scanned the room for

162

a hiding place to put the twenty-one dollars he had on him from working at the sawmill. Noting a hole in the plaster behind a split in the wallpaper, he cautiously worked his way toward it while keeping his eyes fixed on Muzzurree.

"Whatcha keep lookin' at me for?" Muzzurree asked. "Why don't yah get a showah?"

"Thought maybe I could help yah find some clothes."

"Well, I don't need your help. Yah wanted to come here to get cleaned up. Why don't yah get some of that dirt off yah."

"Okay. Just thought I'd help," Scottie said, picking up a pair of overalls and holding them up to himself. "Don't have to be so testy," he murmured while he removed a couple of dollars from the lining of his old jacket. After the money was recovered from his socks and clothes where he had hidden it, he slowly backed up to the corner and slid the money into the pocket made between loose wallpaper and crumbling plaster. The New Testament that Box Car had given him along with his tobacco and matches were shoved under his bedroll.

After throwing his filthy clothes into the "Discard" barrel, Scottie stepped into the shower. He scrubbed his head and watched the dirt run in sheets down his body and into the drain. The warm water caressing his skin was a luxury that made him feel like singing. Scottie stayed in the shower and scrubbed himself until the water began to run cold. By that time, Slim had returned to the room. Muzzurree had disappeared.

"Thank you again for the haircut and clothes and all," Scottie said.

"You're welcome," Slim answered. "It's only because of the generosity of good Christian people that we have clothes to give you." He stared at Scottie's shoes. "Do those shoes fit comfortably? They look rather small."

"I got small feet for my height. These shoes feel like Cinderella's golden slippers to me," he said enthusiastically prancing around. "Could prob'ly walk for months before these soles wear out," he said picking up his foot to look at the bottom like a cowboy examining a horse's hoof. Dancing over near the corner of the room he had hoped he could retrieve his money from behind the wallpaper, but Slim's eyes followed him.

"Service about to begin. Yah better go on out."

"All right," Scottie replied. Turning to pick up his bedroll, he was alarmed that it was nowhere in sight. "Did yah throw away my bedroll?!" he shouted at Slim.

163

"Your buddy that came with yah took it. Said he'd take care of it for yah."

"That bastard," Scottie mumbled seeing that the New Testament was the only thing Muzzurree had left behind. Running to the door, he searched the street, but the man had vanished. Hurrying to the back room of the mission, he hoped to retrieve his money from under the wallpaper before that disappeared too. Slim was still sweeping the floor. All Scottie could do to show his frustration was to kick the pile of clothes and glance toward the wallpaper to make sure none of his money was exposed. Angrily snatching up his New Testament, he head out to the meeting hall.

A thin gray-haired lady was vigorously stomping on the peddles of a pump organ while her hands flowed over the keys as she played the hymns. Parson Troy sat with his head bowed until she stopped playing. He stood after a couple of minutes of silence and said, "Welcome. We are glad to have you all here tonight. There are hymnbooks at the ends of the rows that you may use. We will all stand and sing number 48, 'The Old Rugged Cross.'" One of the men who knew the tunes sang out heartily, while the others mutely held the songbooks in front of them or softly sang notes that were out of key. Another song, "When the Roll is Called up Yonder" was sung. Scottie smiled as he watched the organist's head bob to the rhythm and fast tempo of the song.

When the Parson stood to preach, Scottie's mind wandered back to the time when he was a kid and his family stayed at missions on their way home from Alabama. The feelings he had when sitting with his family on hard benches came flooding back. To keep himself from getting depressed, he thought how fortunate he was to be in a warm and dry building instead of sitting at some railroad station or out in the cold rain waiting for a train. He forced himself to forget the uncomfortable benches along with old Muzzurree's treachery and listen to what the Parson had to say.

"Our passage today is found in the Book of Luke," Parson Troy began. Scottie pulled his New Testament from his shirt, smug in the fact that he had read enough of his scriptures to know where Luke was. The Parson held his Bible high in his right hand, pages flopped open. "We're going to read from the book of Luke, chapter 15, verses 11 through 24."

Pages rustled as some of the men took a Bible from the end of the bench and tried to find the passage. Flipping through his Testament, Scottie found the chapter and ran his finger down the verses until he caught up with the Parson's reading.

It was an interesting story about a boy who asked his father for his inheritance so he could go into the world to find happiness. He squandered all his money on loose living and fickle friends. When the money was gone, so were his friends. The only work he could get was a menial job of feeding pigs. When the boy was desperate enough to eat the husks that were meant for the animals, he decided to go home and humbly ask his father for a job.

The father stood daily by the road watching for his son to return. When he saw him coming, he ran to meet him. Joyfully he welcomed him back with tears of joy and then threw a big party for him. Scottie decided this must be like a fairy tale. He couldn't imagine a father doing anything like that. His Pa would be waiting with a strap in his hand and hatred in his heart if he were to go home.

Staring at the Parson, Scottie became fascinated by the young man's Adam's apple bouncing up and down. Tired of watching and listening, Scottie folded his hands and closed his eyes. He was dozing when the Parson pounded the pulpit and raised his voice.

"God is the Father who loves you! I was like that boy in this parable!" the Parson continued. "I took to riding the rails, just like some of you men. I wanted adventure. I wanted a better life." Now he was getting Scottie's attention. This man dressed so neatly and speaking so well had been a hobo? It didn't seem possible, but he could relate to it. "I found out there was nothing in this world that made me happy." the minister continued, "I was homesick and wished to go home, but I was afraid and ashamed to face my parents. It was then that I met a man who told me about Jesus Christ and a God who loved me. He helped me turn my life and thinking around. I didn't want to run any longer. I wanted to go home and see my father and ask his forgiveness. I wanted to make something of my life."

Scottie continued to listen. He couldn't believe there was a God who wanted to be a loving Father to him, but when the Parson gave an altar call and the organ was softly playing "Just As I Am", he went forward with a couple of others just to find out more. The Parson put his arm around Scottie's shoulders and led him to a side room where he talked with him about God's love. This was something Scottie could not understand. Love and peace were things he hadn't experienced much in his life and it was hard to comprehend such a thing as a loving Heavenly Father waiting for him to come to Him.

"My Pa hates me. He always beat up on me if I didn't obey him. Is God a father like that?"

"No. God loves you. He is waiting for you to come to Him and ask for forgiveness of your sins. He's like the father in the parable who stands watching the road, hoping to see his son come home." The Parson knelt by a chair and started praying for Scottie. Confused as to what was expected of him, he knelt down beside the Parson.

"Why don't you stay around the Mission and work for a week and attend our Bible studies?" the Parson asked as he stood to his feet. "That might help you understand your New Testament more. I notice it means a lot to you."

"It was given me by a good friend," Scottie whispered. Then looking the Parson in the eyes, he said, "I may want to stay around for a few days, but I don't have any money for a bed." He believed he wasn't totally lying because his money was still hidden behind the wallpaper. He wasn't about to leave without it and he wasn't about to spend any of it for a bed.

"Since you've confessed your sins and agreed to change your ways, you can get a job here full time at fifty cents an hour, with four days' lodging and meals before work starts each day."

Scottie didn't realize he'd agreed to change his ways, but the offer of a job seemed tempting to him. Sitting at the table with the other men, his mind was still on the Parson's words. He ate slowly, trying to concentrate on the little pieces of meat and vegetables floating in the stew. All the while his mind bounced back and forth between thinking how nice it would be to have a loving father and what a dirty scum Muzzurree had turned out to be.

"You're makin' a lot of noise eatin' that stew," he said sharply to the man next to him.

"Good stew deserves good sounds," the man answered. "Slurpin' and burpin' lets your hostess know you're enjoyin' the food," he laughingly said as he nudged Scottie's arm. "What's the mattah with yah anyhow?"

"Nothin'," Scottie responded, slamming his fork down on the table.

166

Angrily standing and hoisting his legs over the bench he went outside to smoke and think. When he drifted back inside, he was determined to retrieve his money from its hiding place and hit the road.

"Did you want something in the room?" the Parson asked, coming up behind Scottie who was vigorously shaking the knob on the locked door.

"No. Not really," he stuttered, "Was just goin' to see if there were shoes that fit me bettah than these, but changed my mind. These will do fine."

"Are you sure? I could help you if you wish."

"No. I think I like these. Thank yah anyway."

"Have you thought about staying for a few days?"

"Yeah, I'll hang 'round for a while, but don't want any more charity. I'll sleep on a cardboard on the floor."

"Suit yourself," the Parson said, handing him a blanket. Scottie dragged a large piece of cardboard across the floor positioning himself outside the door of the back room.

****

In the middle of the night Scottie was suddenly awakened by loud hacking and gagging noises which sounded very close to him. Hastily getting to his feet, he crossed to the other side of the room while someone shuffled toward the light switch and other men started moving about.

"What's the mattah, old man?" Slim asked, rushing over to where a bony grey-haired old man was chucking up greenish phlegm onto his scraggly beard. "You look real sick. I bettah get the Parson."

The man stunk so badly that the stench made Scottie gag. Afraid that the man had a contagious disease, he left his cardboard, grabbed the blanket and hastily ran outside. An empty boxcar on the siding served as a place for him to sleep the rest of the night. As soon as the door was opened in the morning, he went back inside the mission.

"Where's the old man?" he asked Slim.

"He died. Didn't yah hear the commotion goin' on durin' the night?"

"Nah. I was sleepin' in a boxcar on the sidin' up the line. What'd he die of?"

"Don't know. Cops said he drank himself to death. They've had run-ins with him 'round the town for years."

"Oh," Scottie uttered, relieved that the man hadn't died of some

167

horrible contagious disease. Noticing the door to the back room open, he saundered over and stepped in. The Parson was sitting with his Bible open on the table. Not wishing to disturb him, Scottie started backing out the door.

"You are an early riser," the Parson said looking at him from over the top of his glasses.

"Yeah, guess so." He wasn't enthused about having to stay, but knew he had to wait until he could find the room unattended. Then he could get his money from in back of the wallpaper and get going.

"Since you've decided to stay, work will begin after breakfast."

"I'll be ready," Scottie said, turning and heading for the dining hall.

Work consisted of baling newspapers and sorting clothes until lunch each day. After a couple of days of this monotonous tedious work he was delighted when a freight hauling bananas came into the yard. Scottie quickly volunteered when the Parson asked someone to clean out the loose bananas that had fallen from the stalks. After scavenging the good produce, the remains were swept up and the inside of the boxcars scrubbed spotless. In exchange for this work the mission kept the loose bananas which were enjoyed raw as well as cooked in many inventive dishes.

Every day at 2:00 p.m. Scottie attended the Bible study. His New Testament was becoming more understandable under the creative explanations of Parson Troy, but he was still restless staying in one place.

"I think I'll be travelin' home," Scottie told the Parson one day when he had found the back room empty. With his twenty-one dollars tucked safely into his clothing, he was itching to get back to riding the rails.

"I'll pray that you get home safely," the Parson said. "This is your pay," he said as he pressed two dollars into Scottie's hand.

"Thank you," Scottie said, turning his back and hustling out of the mission and down the road. Wearing shoes without holes and clean clothes did a lot for his morale. With his hair cut short and free from dirt and lice, and an extra set of clothes tucked under his arm, he thought about heading back to Rhode Island and home.

Riding A Manifest

Although he fully intended to head North when he left the mission, Scottie fell back into his old habits. He jumped on the first train heading out of Tennessee and got caught up in the thrill of the rails again.

Two months later he was walking down a tarred road in Texas. There were only a few puffy clouds scattered across the azure blue sky and very few shade trees. He was tired, hungry and sweaty.

"Hey, Buddy, where'd I find the King?" he asked a man standing beside a shantytown near the freight yard.

"Over there." The man waved his hand limply as though it took all his energy to move.

Rows of amazing, squalid houses ingeniously made from heavy cardboard and various pieces of lumber were "home" for many. Scottie envisioned pushing the shack at the end of the row and seeing them all topple over like dominoes. The odors from cooking pots, clothes soaking in tepid water, and nearby privies filled the air. Striding over the parched ground, he was amazed at the number of men, women and kids living there. The young children played naked in the street.

Sitting in the shade of a clump of trees at the end of the town was a group of unkempt, smelly men. In the center of this grimy bunch was a man resting in a hammock made from an old blanket tied between two large shade trees. This king looked at Scottie through half-closed eyelids.

"Can yah tell me when's the next freight pulling out headin' North?"

"They just started firin' 'er up on the sidin' over there. Takes 'bout ten hours to get a full head of steam. I'd guess they'll be leavin' 'bout ten tonight, but yah not gonna ride that one," the King grunted. "Word's out that it's goin' to be a manifest loaded with the fuzz that'll be armed

169

with 38's. That's the gospel and yah bettah wait 'til mornin'. Might be 'nother one headin' in then. Can hang 'round here if yah like."

"Much obliged, but if a train's goin' North tonight, so am I." Scottie set his jaw. Securely locked, heavily guarded cars would not change his mind. He was heading home.

"Good luck, kid. Don't say yah ain't been warned!"

"I'll find a way to ride it!" he defiantly hollered over his shoulder as he headed out of Shantytown toward the main road.

"Look for a green house 'bout a mile back, boy!" one of the men called. "They're good for a handout. Guess your last meal might's well be a good one!"

"Smart ass," Scottie mumbled.

****

Staying out of sight at the edge of the freight yard, Scottie watched the swollen orange sun sink behind the misty gray clouds. Soon the sky was dark with only one ribbon of golden sunlight hanging to the horizon and the stars were beginning to fill the sky. He carefully crawled toward the train station.

His stomach was full of small "pig potatoes" that he had found discarded in a freshly dug field. After eating all he could of these raw potatoes, he had filled his pockets. Later on he intended to make a fire and fry them. A few late apples from a gnarled tree had been his dessert. Although he had walked several miles, he never saw a green house; or house of any color for that matter. But, he had not expected to. A group of hoboes hanging around the same area wouldn't give away their meal tickets to a stranger.

Two rows of Model A's were lined up in the parking area at the station. Slinking behind the cars, he eyeballed the contents of each auto. As he crouched beside one fliver, a handsome knitted afghan with multi-colored stripes caught his eye. Speedily fetching it out through the open window, he leaped behind a large tree trunk where he rolled this newly acquired possession inside his khaki bedroll. Then he took an inconspicuous position on the ground where he could study the manifest.

The King had known what he was talking about. The train was now on the main track preparing to move out. It was crawling with railroad bulls, some armed with guns; the rest twirled billy clubs by their sides as their eyes carefully scanned the yard. Scottie knew they wouldn't hesitate to crack his skull if they caught him getting on the manifest. But then, if he were killed, who would care?

By the time the stars filled the sky, Scottie had figured his strategy. He felt confident that he could hop on the freight and not be seen. Waiting until the cops were away from the gondola he had chosen, he moved with precision. Rolling over the narrow edge of the flat car he lay face down under a cement mixer. Not daring to move a muscle, he listened to cinders crunching and stones rolling under the feet of men walking beside the the train. He waited until the train gave a jerk and started slowly down the stone lined tracks. With the help of the chains holding the cement mixer to the gondola, he leaped into the bowl which was tipped so that the opening faced the sky. The stolen afghan served as a buffer when he curled up inside the hard unyielding metal blades. His heart pounded as the light from a lantern shone into the mixer as someone paced the length of the shallow freight car. Gradually the manifest picked up speed and with an occasional long whistle at each crossing, went thundering through the night. Scottie felt safe now as he nibbled on raw potatoes and withered apples while gazing at the stars.

Bouncing around inside the cement mixer hurt his back. It made him think of the times when his father couldn't afford a mule or horse to plow the garden. Pa had made up a contraption that he strapped to him and his brother. They pulled the plow through hard unyielding soil while his Pa held the handles and tried to keep them on a straight line with cussing and whacks across their backs. He wondered if his father had changed and would welcome him home. Nah, it would never happen. He chuckled at the thought. He had to face the probability that he would be thrown out of the house on his ass if his Pa could still handle him.

He was so excited about heading home that he couldn't relax. His mind raced with thoughts of how great it would be to see Ma and his friend Floyd again. He remembered the time he and Floyd had taken Floyd's father's car without his say so. Floyd was short for a boy of 13 and could hardly see out the windshield. Because they didn't dare go down the road where his father might see him, Floyd had taken to the woods. Scottie smiled as he thought of that car flying down that hill, dodging the rocks and weaving in and out until the car eventually got stuck between two trees and had to be left there. The next day Floyd had grinned and said, "My dad walloped me good, but he was madder about his fliver gettin' scratched than he was whether I got hurt or not."

"How come you're laughin' about it?" Scottie had asked.

"Just funny that's all. Pa doesn't hit harder than swatting a fly anyhow." Floyd sure was lucky having a father like that.

After a while, Scottie fell to meditating on what Parson Troy had said about God loving him. He tried to picture himself in the same situation as the boy in the Bible who had been welcomed home by his father. Being on the rails for so long had softened Scottie's hatred for his Pa. Never having been touched gently by his father, he believed he would really like it if his father gave him a hug. It would certainly be a miracle if they could at least get along for a while. Again, he wouldn't let himself believe something like that would ever happen, so he dismissed it with a shake of his head. He felt it was best to expect the worst and then he wouldn't be disappointed.

When the whistle blew and he could feel the slowing of the train, he stiffly crawled to the top of the bowl and stuck his head out like a groundhog testing for the coming of Spring. Forcing his stiff aching body out of the mixer, he jumped from the gondola, and hustled off into the brush. Having ridden the manifest and not gotten caught was something to brag about. At times like this, he wished he had someone to talk to and share these things with.

As the morning sun heralded a new day, Scottie spotted a piece of cardboard, dragged it into the bushes, and slept soundly until the sun was high in the sky. Still a little stiff, he washed in a nearby stream before limping down the road. Spotting a modest looking home, he went to the back door and knocked.

He smiled as a woman opened the door. "Please, M'am, could yah help me on my way home? I'd be willin' to work for a bite to eat."

His day had begun.

A Man Called Lightnin'

The large rectangular steel hull lined with wide oil streaked vertical boards rattled and shook as the train heading North rushed boldly through the countryside. Even with the door slid half-way open, the vibrations made Scottie feel like he was sitting inside a drum. He looked around at the group of people that had hopped on the boxcar with him. A man with a woman and child sat by themselves in the corner. Three men squatted with their backs against the wall, watching the scenery and commenting on the brilliant Autumn leaves still clinging to the trees. Scottie decided to join two men sitting in the doorway with their legs dangling.

"Why yah got all that clothin' on old man? It ain't that cold today!" one man in back of Scottie shouted.

Scottie turned to see who he was talking to. One of the men against the wall was bald and wore no hat. His face crinkled up like a rumpled paper bag as he grinned, showing toothless gums. A buttonless coat covered a zipped up baggy red sweater. Spilling out from the top of the sweater was a tattered plaid collar. That was partially hidden by a faded bandana tied around his scrawny neck. Long sleeves, which did not belong to the sweater, shirt, or jacket drooped down, covering his hands. All this clothing gave one the impression that he had dressed this way on purpose to look like a clown.

"Best way to carry your belongin's is on your back--that way I ain't forgettin' them or havin' someone like you snitch 'em on me," the man replied goodnaturedly.

"Old man like you should be home somewhere restin', not scuttlin' 'round the country," another man said sympathetically.

"Well, Old Tatters ain't got no other home to go to. This be my life now. I'll ride the rails 'til my Maker calls me home."

"I know how yah feel, Tatters," the man with the wife and child said."Goldie and me had no life where we come from. Both from poor families who got caught in the dust bowl out west. The land couldn't support us so we took to riding the rails." The woman hugged the young girl tighter to her and shyly hung her head. "Me and my wife gonna make sure our little Sarah is cared for even if we travel the country like nomads until I can find a job."

"Well, let me tell yah 'bout my childhood," Tatters shouted above the rumbling underneath as the wheels clacked on the rails.

"You fellas ain't had it bad at all," he chattered. "Why when I was a youngun' we had to scoop handfuls of mosquitos off the watah bucket just to get a stagnant drink. Come to think of it," Tatters laughed, "we ate those bugs for suppah when meat was low."

"The shack my father built for us to live in was worse than some shanties in the jungles," he continued. "We didn't have no fancy cabin by a babbling brook, but we did have runnin' watah. Every time it rained the watah ran in under the door and across the dirt floor to a hole out the other side. We had a brook runnin' right through our kitchen! Us kids enjoyed that. Sure felt good squishin' mud up 'tween our toes as we walked 'cross the floor."

"Tatters, you're puttin' us on. No one had it that bad."

"Yes sir, I did!" Tatters yelled indignantly. "We survived on air and hard work -- plus what we could make grow in a pitiful little patch about yea by yea," he said extending his hands about 3' by 3' apart.

The men laughed. Even Scottie had to chuckle as he tried to envision what Tatters was talking about.

"My brother and me slept up in the rafters on hay for beddin'. Got wet every time it rained from leaks in the roof. When it didn't rain, the hay got wet anyway from my brother peeing the bed." Tatters chuckled as he reminisced. "Threw our beddin' out every mornin' and started with a whole new bed the next day. Nevah had a sheet on my bed in my life."

"Ridin' the rails is a picnic compared to what we left behind," the man with the wife said sitting up and leaning forward. Tatters, still grinning, ignored him, slumped down, curled up in a ball, and started snoring.

"Guess Old Tatters don't want to hear your story," one man said. Several chuckled while the embarrassed man glowered at them and put his arm protectively around his wife.

****

"Do yah smoke?" Scottie asked a small dark guy sitting near him.

"When I can get the makin's," he replied.

"Help yahself," Scottie said, handing him his tobacco pouch.

"Thank yah," the man said, eagerly rolling a smoke.

"Yah got a handle?"

"Sure 'nuf. They calls me Lightnin'."

"Pretty fast, huh?" Scottie said, blowing a spiral of smoke into the air.

"Hafta be. Learned that down in Mississippi."

"Cops evah catch yah?"

"They tried mighty hard, but my legs carried me out of their reach, leavin' them huffin' for breath." Lightnin' drew a big breath. "It wasn't just cops aftah me either. I had to outrun a shotgun more than once when I asked for a job or somethin' to eat. Just 'cause I got dark skin, women grabbed their kids by the arms and pulled them to othah side of the road when they saw me comin'. They'd stare at me with their eyelids all squinted up, watchin' me like I was gonna kill them or kidnap their younguns."

Scottie quietly watching the scenery flash by, but his mind was on Lightnin' and dark skinned folks. He knew the hatred his father felt for them and he could imagine how Lightnin' would be treated if he ever came to the door of his parents' house. To get his mind off his father, he asked Lightnin', "Whatcha been livin' off of?"

"Plenty of potatoes laying in the fields. Ate them raw or fried up if I could steal myself a little oil." Lightnin' smiled. "Many a farmer helped me out by havin' fruit trees planted where I could help myself without their permission."

"Yeah, I've eaten plenty of potatoes, too. That along with berries and fruit made up my meals many a time. Course I had to steal them like you, but what the hey? We gotta live." Scottie snuffed out his butt and asked, "Where yah headin'? Anyplace special?"

"Nah. Just wanted to get out of the South and see how people up North lived."

"I'm headin' home to Rhode Island," Scottie volunteered. Lightnin' nodded and then crawled back and sat against the swaying side of the

175

boxcar. Scottie followed him and lay on his back on the floor. Using his bedroll for a pillow, he got a good view of the scenery.

"Why don't yah go home?" Scottie asked.

"Didn't get 'long with my old man. I never did anythin' right 'cording to him."

"Guess you and me got somethin' in common. Both got stuck with sonsobitches for fathers."

After staring out the boxcar door for a while, Scottie suddenly sat up. "That Model T makes me think of home!" he exclaimed. He watched as a fliver traveled along a dirt road parallel to the track.

"How's that? Yah live in a car?" Lightnin' jokingly replied.

"Ha. Ha. Very funny. When I was about seven my Pa had a Model 'T' that took my family all the way to Florida. I hated the long ride. When we got there he lost the car to the ocean."

"Sittin' in the car warn't like the open space of a freight was it? I hate bein' in confined spaces."

"Well," Scottie said, "it weren't all bad. We did have some good times." He didn't want Lightnin' feeling sorry for him.

"Like what?"

Scottie tried to think of something good about the trip.

"We laughed a lot when my Pa drove backwards up a hill."

"What'd he do that for?"

"The Model T got half way up the hill and then quit runnin'. My Pa let it roll back down the hill." Scottie remembered how tense he had felt, knowing that his father would have to blame someone for the car's inability to climb and fearing that he would be the one he punished. "The gas level was too low in the tank for the gas to reach the carburetor. Pa turned the "T" 'round and climbed up the hill in reverse. Other cars facin' us blew their horns and waved. It wasn't 'til we got to the top that Pa got out, all irritated, and swore and kicked the car 'til he was jumpin' 'round holdin' his foot and complainin' he'd broke his toe."

"Your father had a bad temper?" Lightnin' chuckled.

"That's the truth," Scottie stated bluntly.

****

The weather hadn't been so bad the first winter when Scottie rode the rails. Every day he had found a jungle, barn, or a make-shift shelter. If all else failed, the Salvation Army halls had been kind to him. When the train stopped in Pennsylvania, it was the middle of November.

Scottie's shoes had cracked and split open on the sides allowing the two pairs of socks he had pulled over each other to bulge out and drag on the ground. His other clothing was ragged and getting thin.

"Mind if I tag along with yah a while?" Lightnin' asked as the rest of the hoboes scattered down the streets of the city.

"Okay by me, but we gotta find some place to get warm," Scottie chattered through clinking teeth. Although he still had some money hidden on him, he wouldn't think of spending it for shoes or a night's lodging. The only thing he had bought was tobacco, and then only doled out the few cents needed. The fierce winds funneling down the alleys and corridors of the city swirled papers around them and blew dirt into their eyes. Walking with heads down and bodies bent forward, they hustled along as the wind whipped their backsides.

"Let's see what we can find in here," Lightnin' said dodging into an alley behind a restaurant. Stray cats yowled as they were swatted away from the garbage cans with a stick by the two humans who needed to scavenge.

"What are you two doing in there?!" a policeman yelled.

"Nothin'," Scottie answered. "Just tryin' to get warm."

"You can't be bumming around this city. Best get on your way!" The man's menacing tone, along with his drawn gun, was enough to send Scottie and Lightnin' running out onto the street at the other end of the alley. They ran a few blocks before daring to duck into another alley.

"Tell yah what," Lightnin' said as he picked up a bunch of old newspapers. "Stuff these in your clothes. Keeps yah warm. Ins'lates yah." When they had finished crumpling up papers and stuffing them down their pant legs and inside their jackets, they continued searching through trash cans.

"Yah look awful fat and bulgy," Scottie laughed.

"Yeah, newspapers fill me out just fine," Lightnin' said, running his hands down the bulges of paper.

"Instant fat," Scottie chuckled, patting his bulging stomach.

"Lookee here!" Lightnin' called, picking up a "Hot Peppers" jar and shaking up the juice left in it. After taking a swig, he passed the jar to Scottie who turned it around in his hands and stared at it, wondering whether to drink it or not.

"Go 'head. Take a swig. It'll warm your insides," Lightnin' said.

177

Scottie tipped back his head and gingerly let a little of the hot juice run down his gullet.

"Whoo-ee! That's hot stuff!" he shouted. His mouth felt like he had swallowed a fireball.

"It's just puttin' fire in your belly. Yah'll feel warm for a while." The two of them drank the pepper juice while eating scraps of food that had come from other people's plates. Then they walked the streets for the rest of the day.

In the evening they trudged past the large red and gray brick buildings. The store windows were decorated with Christmas displays. Ragged children stared wide-eyed at the toys. Scottie's heart was heavy with memories of unhappy holidays that had come and gone with his family. He stopped to watch a shiny metal train winding its way over the tracks and through the tunnels laid out in a window. What a contrast it was to his wooden train with a broken wheel he had played with when a child. The hurtful recollection of his father angrily throwing it into the wood fire caused him to turn and run down the sidewalk like a wild animal. Lightnin' followed at his heels.

"Sure took off in a hurry. What ailed yah?"

"Not a thing," Scottie stated positively. "Just felt like seein' if yah really was fast as lightnin'."

"Well yah found out, so let's stop runnin'."

As they jogged, a man carrying a small tree walked toward them. Three children were skipping along behind him. The scene made Scottie sad. It made him think of the little trees his Mother had brought into the house during the holidays. She didn't have many decorations or many presents but she had tried to give them a happy memory.

"Sally's House!" Scottie exclaimed as he pointed to a building across the square. A single string of Christmas lights outlined the door and a large sign above the door read "Salvation Army. All Welcome."

"Let's go over and get warmed up," Scottie said. "We can get some food and clean clothes too."

"Here's where I leave yah," Lightnin' announced. "Don't intend to get religion. Wants no part of their charity."

"Don't be silly," Scottie said. "They'll give yah somethin' even if yah don't want religion." Looking back over his shoulder, he discovered he was talking to himself for Lightnin' had disappeared. Scottie called his name but there was no answer. With no desire to stay out in the cold any longer than necessary, he rushed to the mission door and stepped inside.

A dozen or so rough looking men sat solemnly on the wooden benches. Scottie's frost-bitten feet tingled painfully from the warmth of the wood stove. While stomping his feet and rubbing his hands together over the fire he was aware of the men staring at him. It was then that he remembered he still had the newspapers stuffed into his clothes. These bunches here and there must have looked funny to them, but he didn't care. He had no more pride or shyness. They had to have something to look at and it might as well be him. After getting warmed up, he started pulling the newspapers out and throwing them into the stove.

"That's one smart boy," one man said, winking at another man.

"Sure is. Looks kinda skinny though when he gets all his insulation out of his clothes."

Scottie just looked at them and grinned.

"You are invited to stay to the evening service, after which we will have a Thanksgiving dinner," the preacher announced.

"Can't refuse that offer," Scottie said, especially since the aroma of the turkey roasting in the oven made his mouth water. He had barely gotten clean clothes when it was time for the evening service. His stomach growled as he sat through the long sermon while trying not to think of the food waiting for him when the final "Amen" was said.

He gobbled turkey with all the trimmings into his stomach until he couldn't take another bite. He felt as stuffed as he must have looked before discarding the newspapers.

"Can yah tell me where the trains come through?" he asked the preacher after he had rested a short while. "I'd like to be gettin' home."

With the directions mapped out in his mind, he once more headed for the rails with the hope of finding a train headed closer to Rhode Island and home.

Altoona Pass

Stepping back into the dark, cold winter night, Scottie discovered the wind had picked up and it was snowing. Mountains loomed black off to his right. Approaching the rail yard, his eyes squinted through the swirling white flakes as he searched the length of a freight train. He hoped for an open boxcar or a place to ride that would be out of the wind. Nothing. No place to crawl into. No blinds to sit behind.

In desperation he approached the brakeman. "Please, mister, I'm on my way home to Rhode Island. Could yah let me inside a boxcar?" he begged. The man turned and stared at him with penetrating eyes. Not knowing what the man would do, Scottie instinctively stepped back out of his reach.

"You know better, boy. I feel sorry for your kind, but no way. My job's at stake." With these words, he turned his back and busily checked the couplings.

With only thoughts of getting on that train, Scottie ran to the train's engine. Climbing up to the top step, he banged on the window until the engineer looked his way.

"Please, mister, let me ride inside. I'm freezin'!" The man shook his head.

"I've got a little money. I'll pay yah. You can have all I got! Please!"

"Not allowed," the engineer said. Scottie hopped down onto the gravel bed. He glanced up at the window as the engineer opened it a crack and called out, "If yah got money, buy a ticket on a passenger train!"

Crushed, Scottie retreated into the station. Cautiously surveying the room, he was satisfied that no one was watching when he hurried into the men's room and hastily took money from its hiding places throughout his clothing. He studied it, weighing the fact that he wished

180

with all his heart to take it to his mother against the notion he might be able to get a passenger ticket with it. When he approached the ticket agent, the man looked over the top of his glasses at him. Scottie could tell it irked the man to even talk him. But he smiled and tried to be courteous, thinking perhaps the agent had had a bad day.

"I would like a ticket to Rhode Island, sir," Scottie said.

"No passenger train until tomorrow," the ticket agent snarled. "Got any money?" The ticket agent leaned out the window and studied Scottie. Although he had cleaned up at the mission, he realized that his baggy second hand clothes and bedroll slung over his shoulder told the ticket agent exactly what he was.

"Yeah, I got money," Scottie answered testily. "Whatcha starin' at me for?"

"Nothing. Let's see your money." Then the agent mumbled, "Prob'ly won't let you ride with decent folk anyway."

Scottie doubled his fist and clamped his mouth tightly shut. He had to hold his feelings in control if he was to get a ticket or help from this man.

"Is this enough for a ticket?" Scottie asked, placing his money on the ledge of the window.

"Nope, not enough," the man said after casually thumbing through it. "You best wait and take your chances riding a freight out of here tomorrow. Imagine you're quite adept at that." The man smirked as he handed the money back. Scottie's face grew hot. He tried to get information from the man while anxiously watching out the window to make sure the freight wasn't leaving without him.

"When does that freight leave?" Scottie asked.

"Like it says on the schedule on the wall," the man declared, "in a half hour." Then he emphasized his words, "*but you aren't going to ride on it.*"

"Guess not," Scottie said. Walking slowly to the window, he studied the train again, still hoping to find a place where he could ride. Then he saw it. A tanker. A plan came to his mind as he remembered how he and Rod had ridden on the outside of a tanker. But that had been in warm weather. This train would be going through the Altoona Pass and he was taking an awful chance trying to hang onto an icy rail while keeping his footing on a snow covered metal catwalk. Nevertheless, he was determined to try.

"Could I borrow your pencil for a minute?" he asked the agent.

"Well, yeah, but use it right here where I can keep an eye on you," the agent said as he reluctantly held the tip of the pencil making sure his hand didn't touch Scottie's.

"I ain't gonna take off with it," Scottie replied. Sitting on a bench in front of the ticket window, he took out his New Testament and carefully wrote on the flyleaf: *"Dear Mom, I may never see you again but I want you to know I love you. Whatever dollars are in my clothes are for you. Please don't think bad of me for running away. Your son, Edward."* Then on the endpaper he printed his name and address before carefully tucking it inside his shirt pocket. Returning the pencil to its owner, he said, "Thank you," and headed outside.

He already had all his clothing layered on his body. A pair of knitted mittens had been given to him at the mission for which he was thankful. When the brakemen and railroad bulls crawled inside the cars, he took off his belt which was long enough to wrap around his thin body twice and headed for the tanker. Climbing onto the catwalk, he quickly looped the belt around the handrail and buckled it tightly to his waist. Feeling the train jolt, he knew it was too late to change his mind. He was in it for the long haul.

Tandem engines pulled the train up over the mountain. Slowly it chugged and clacked its way upward. Scottie felt the cold metal as he pressed his body against the tanker. When it started down the slope, speeding through the pass, icy winds tore their way through his clothing. His hands were soon numb from the cold. Resigning himself to the fact that he was going to die, he prayed that God would let someone find his dead body who would return it, along with the New Testament, to his mother.

Not caring whether the belt held his weight or not, he stuffed his mittens inside his pocket and lowered his hands so he could urinate on them. The warm pee put feeling into his hands long enough for him to put on his mittens and pull his hands up into his coat sleeves. That way he could use the ends of the sleeves for added protection from the icy rail.

He fought the inclination to sleep by concentrating on dragging himself up and down the catwalk from one end of the tanker to the other. Although trying to stay alert, the cold was winning the battle. He was semi-conscious when the train pulled into the station at Providence. With no feeling in his hands, he fumbled a few minutes with the belt buckle before it loosened, sending him plummeting to the frozen ground. Squinting, he tried to focus on the station sitting on the opposite side of the tracks. His foggy brain was alert enough to know he had to get inside. Stumbling on half-frozen painful feet was agony but he made it across the tracks and fell through the door of the station onto the floor.

When he regained consciousness, a man was kneeling beside him rubbing his arms and hands.

"Where did you come from young man?" he asked.

Scottie didn't answer him fearing that he was a policeman.

"Well, someone said they saw you riding in on the tanker. It's a wonder you didn't die from exposure," the man said as he shook his head. "You must have been mighty desperate to get to Rhode Island."

"I was," Scottie mumbled. He shakily stood up and stomped his feet on the floor. Although his head was dizzy, he tried to make it to the door. He didn't like the attention he was getting in this place.

"You must be very hungry," the man said as he grabbed Scottie's arm and led him to a bench. "Eat this sandwich and drink this before you start out." The man already had the cap off of his thermos and was pouring the hot coffee. Scottie ravenously gulped down the sandwich and drank the black coffee.

"Thanks for your kindness," he said handing the cup back to the man. "I gotta get hitchhikin' now. I gotta get home."

"Where's home?"

"East Greenwich."

"That's near where I'm going. I'll give you a lift."

Scottie had never expected such good fortune. He quickly lowered his head so that the man couldn't see how deeply this gesture had affected him. "Thank you. Thank you very much," he said after he gained his composure. "Could I give you a little money for your food and the ride?"

"That's nice of you to offer, but I really don't need any money. I'm going that way anyway and I'd enjoy the company."

As they climbed into the Model A, Scottie sank back onto the seat and said a prayer of thanks to God for this helpful man. The man rattled on about this and that, but Scottie didn't feel like talking and tuned him out. The boy had too many other things on his mind and could care less what was being said. Eventually, they settled down into a silence broken only by the purr of the Model A's engine. When the car stopped, Scottie hopped out and with another "Thank you" headed up the darkened road, ready to hitchhike should another car come along.

It felt good to be back in familiar territory again, but it was late and dark clouds washed across the moon. Under the cover of night, he walked past houses with darkened windows and ran by empty fields. No cars were coming down the road this late at night so he searched for a place to sleep until daybreak. An abandoned house with the doors and windows tightly boarded caught his eye. He yanked and pulled on the boards until his fingers were sore, but couldn't break the nails free. Desperately circling the house trying to find a way to get in, he discovered a rather large dog house out in back. Crawling in he curled up to spend the night, thankful to be out of the wind. He immediately fell asleep from exhaustion. That night he dreamed of a happy homecoming.

That night Scottie slept in an abandoned doghouse.

The Reception

Scottie's emotions went from hope that his family still lived in the same house to fear of what his father's reaction would be to his returning home. He walked slowly the last few miles up the snow-covered road for his ribs felt like they would split at any minute, causing his body to explode. While wrestling with the desire to turn back to the rails, he heard a voice called out to him several times.

"Edward! Edward! Is that you, Edward!"

Scottie turned, surprised to see Floyd's mother in the yard so early in the morning.

"It's me, alright," Scottie said. "I haven't been called Edward for a while now, that's why it didn't register in my brain right away."

"What's your name now?" she laughed. "And where yah been keepin' yourself?" He ignored her question as to his name.

"I've been hoboing across the county." He smiled as he started across the lawn to where she was throwing seeds on the ground for the birds. "Is Floyd at home?"

"No. Floyd joined the Army a couple of months back. I'll give you his address if you'd like to write to him," she offered. "He really would have loved to see you."

Scottie couldn't hide his disappointment at not being able to see Floyd. Damn him anyway! All the stories he had planned on telling him would have to wait.

"I'd bettah get on and see my Ma," he mumbled as he turned back to the road. "They still livin' in the same house?"

"Far as I know. They're not much for visitin' you know."

"Yeah, I know. Tell Floyd I said hi."

With his heart beating rapidly, he trudged up the driveway toward the house that looked so much smaller than he remembered it. He

185

awkwardly knocked on the door of his family's house much as he had done at the door of strangers. Out of habit, he stepped back away from the door and waited when he heard movement inside.

When Jane appeared at the door, her face turned so white Scottie thought she was going to faint. Because she stood staring at him with her hand over her heart, he wasn't sure that she recognized him. He knew he must look horrible with his ragged clothes and long uncombed hair.

"Mom," he said softly and smiled.

"It's really you! Edward!" she cried, coming to life and excitedly hugging him and crying all the while.

"Guess I look pretty awful to yah, huh?"

"Never in a million years would you look awful to me." She tightly held to his arm and pulled him inside. "Come in and get warm. Get something to eat. You look as skinny as a bone."

Parnell, Laura and Candice looked up from their breakfast of oatmeal and toast. Their eyes stared at the wayward family member whom they hardly recognized. Scottie felt a nervous tension in the air as he sat down and tried to make light conversation with the children. His Mother kept smiling and asking him questions which he didn't feel like answering. So far this home coming wasn't anything like he had imagined.

"Where's Pa?" he asked.

"He's sleepin'. He'll be up shortly."

A loud hacking and retching of Coop's cigarette cough could be heard upstairs.

"Guess he's awake now," Scottie said. "Before he comes down I want yah to know that I'd like to be called Scottie instead of Edward."

"What! Why should I do that?"

"I just been tellin' people that's my name while ridin' the rails. I kinda like it. Do you think it would be all right if the kids called me Scottie?"

"Sure, I'll call yah that," Laura said with a grin.

Seeing the stricken look on his mother's face, Scottie suddenly felt uncomfortable. "You can still call me Edward, Mom. Just wanted to let yah know," he mumbled.

Feeling like he shouldn't have come here, he found it difficult to wait to see his pa. He forced himself to stay seated as he slowly ate the toast his mother handed him. He had come this far and didn't want to leave until he had made an effort to make things right between him and his father if possible. As he was thinking about what he would say to his pa, there was a familiar creaking of the stairs. Jane flitted restlessly around the kitchen hurrying to get the children out the door and off to school while Coop stood at the foot of the stairs and glared at Scottie.

"How are you sir?" Scottie asked politely.

"Decided to come home did yah?" Coop snarled.

"I won't be stayin' long," Scottie assured him, walking toward him to shake his hand. Coop did not move.

"Coop, Edward has come home," Jane said as she started crying. "This is your son, Coop. It wouldn't hurt you to be civil to him."

Scottie continued to hold his hand out, ready to greet his father. Coop looked so tired and old that all the fear Scottie ever had for him vanished in that moment. He couldn't believe that he had ever feared this pitiful looking man. He would like to put his arms around Pa, and tell him he was sorry, but Coop gave him no opportunity. His father limply held his son's hand as though it was distasteful to even touch him, like he was holding the tail of a rotten fish.

"Ragged lookin' bastard ain't yah?" Coop snapped.

Scottie could see the hatred was still alive in his father. Before any more could be said, Coop turned and stomped up the stairs, slamming the bedroom door behind him.

"I can see there'd be nothin' but trouble if I stayed," Scottie said sadly. "I can see how it is with Pa. I'll be leavin' soon's I can clean up. I just wanted to come and see yah and let yah know I'm all right. Pa won't come out of his room again 'til I leave. I wouldn't want to cause yah any more trouble." His eyes brimmed with tears.

"Please stay," Jane said as she wept and hugged him tightly.

"I love yah, Mom, but there's no life here for me. I've got to make something of myself. I'll be leavin'. There's nothin' here for me now."

"Where'll you go?" Jane asked frantically. "Back to the trains?"

"Nah. Floyd's mom said he joined the Army. I think I'll be headin' into town and joinin' up too. I'll keep in touch. I'll even be able to send yah some money."

While Scottie washed up, his mother found him some clean clothes and insisted he take a packed lunch with him.

"Here's somethin' I'd like yah to have," Scottie said as he took his

187

prized New Testament out of his shirt pocket. "A real good friend gave it to me. I'd like yah to have it along with the few dollars I have left from workin' in a saw mill a while back in New Mexico."

"But you'll need the money," Jane objected.

"Nah. Army'll take care of me. I'll goin' to make somethin' of myself. I promise."

Jane opened the New Testament and flipped through its pages. Then she started reading the scrawled hand written message on the flyleaf out loud. *"Dear Mom, I may never see you again but I want you to know I love you..."* With tears trickling down her cheeks, she bravely stood in the doorway holding the New Testament and trying to smile as she waved goodbye to her son. He swung around and left, not daring to look back.

The first time Scottie had left home he ran in fear. This time he straightened his shoulders and with determination marched down the drive with a confidence that he could weather whatever storms should come into his life. He would no longer be known as Edward, son of "Crazy Coop." He would be Scottie, a survivor, for the rest of his life.*

~ ~ ~ ~ ~ ~ ~ ~

* See page 195.

BIBLIOGRAPHY

Ball, Don Jr., *America's Colorful Railroads,* a Pictorial History of the Rail's Transition from Steam to Diesel, Bonanza Books, NY.

Holbrook, Stewart H. *The Story of American Railroads,* Crown Publishers, NY, 1947.

Leuchtenburg, Wm. E. *et al,* Time-Life Books. *New Deal and War,* Vol. II: 1933-1945, Time-Life Books, NY.

"Long Hitch-Hike Home," *The Providence Sunday-Journal Magazine,* November 16, 1930.

Mathers, Michael, *Riding the Rails,* Gambit, Boston, 1973.

Morgan and Dykas, "To Be Homeless in Winter," *The Providence Journal,* December 30, 1993, A-1.

National Geographic Society, *Railroads, The Great American Adventure.*

Reiman, Roy, "The Day a Hobo Called Me," *Reminisce,* Jan./Feb. 1995, p. 20.

Terkel, Studs, pseud., *Hard Times,* An Oral History of the Great Depression, Pantheon Books, Div. of Random House, NY.

This Fabulous Century, Time-Life Books, NY, 1969, pp. 234,236.

Union Station Trust Fund, "Speaking of Union Station," 1 Commerce Place, Nashville, TN 37219.

Videos
National Geographic, <u>Love Those Trains,</u> Vestron Video.

Skyfire, <u>Riding the Rails</u> on America's Most Beautiful Steam Engine, 1775 Kuenzli Ln, Reno, NV 89502.

Superior Promotions, <u>Thunder On the Rails,</u> Produced by Skyfire, Reno, NV 1990

Riding the Rails

I've ridden the "reefers," box cars too,
tankers and gondolas, to name a few.

I've ridden the blinds with fear in my heart;
knowing one false move and from this life
      I'd depart.

Alone on a freight train roaring through
      the night
is a lonely adventure for a boy taking
      flight.

Clickity-clack-clickity-clack-clickity-clack
I wonder if I'll ever be going back.

                by Scottie

GLOSSARY

OF WORDS USED BY HOBOES

BANJO - frying pan

BINDLE - bedroll

BLINDS - fabric inbetween engine and first car on passenger trains

BOXCARS - enclosed and covered railway car for the transportation of freight

DINGBAT - an experienced, knowledgeable hobo

GAYCAT - one inexperienced at riding the rails or at hoboing

GONDOLA - open, shallow freight car

HIGHBALLING - railroad signal indicating full speed ahead

JUNGLED UP - bumming around town

MANIFEST - a train that was securely locked and guarded, usually carrying perishable goods

PUT THE RIGGING ON - begging for food

RAILROAD BULL - policeman who patroled the trains and yards

REEFER - the two ends of a refrigerator car where ice was stored to keep produce cold

SALLY'S - Salvation Army

SPIKES - wedges used to secure the boxcar doors while the freight was in motion.

THOUSAND-MILE PAPER - a waterproof paper used around lumber yards, picked up by hoboes for insulation and protection from the weather.

WATER TOWER - towers along the rail route where trains stopped to take on water

YEGGS - hoboes turned thieves who were destructive to both trains and hobo jungles. Their lawless acts gave hoboes a bad name.

HOBO CODE
SYMBOLS AND WHAT THEY MEANT TO OTHER HOBOES

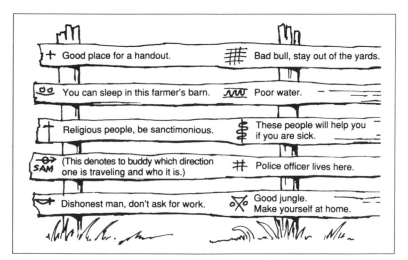

Used by permission of *Reminisce Magazine*

MEANING OF TRAIN WHISTLES:

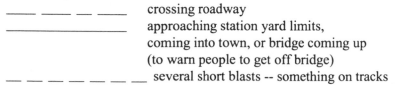

___ ___ __ ___   crossing roadway

_____   approaching station yard limits,
coming into town, or bridge coming up
(to warn people to get off bridge)

_ __ __ __ __ __ __ __   several short blasts -- something on tracks

Scottie joined the United States Army at the age of 17.
He was stationed in Hawaii on December 7, 1941.
He is a Pearl Harbor survivor.

Scottie and Stella together raised five sons and one daughter
and have twelve grandchildren.

As entrepreneurs, they started and ran several businesses,
among which is the well known *South County Spectator*
which they sold in 1980. It is still going strong.

They are both active in church and community affairs.

ORDER FORM
please print

Name _____

Address _____

City _____

State _____ Zip Code _____

Please send me ____(s) copies of *The Lonesome Whistle's Call* @ $9.95 each			
Add 7% Tax for State of R.I.			
Shipping (see chart)			
TOTAL			

For library rates please write to address below.

Shipping Rates
1 book $2.00
2-3 books $3.00
4+ books $5.00

PLEASE PAY BY CASHIER'S CHECK
OR MONEY ORDER PAYABLE TO:
KINGSTON PRESS
P O Box 86, West Kingston, RI 02892-0086